General Studies

General Studies
An AS and A-level course text

VICTOR WATTON and DICK HOBSON

edited by DAVID WALTON

Hodder & Stoughton
A MEMBER OF THE HODDER HEADLINE GROUP

Orders : please contact Bookpoint Ltd, 130 Milton Park, Abingdon, Oxon OX14 4SB. Telephone: (44) 01235 400414, Fax: (44) 01235 400454. Lines are open from 9.00–6.00 pm, Monday to Saturday, with a 24-hour message answering service. Email address: orders@bookpoint.co.uk

British Library Cataloguing in Publication Data

A catalogue record for this title is availale from The British Library

ISBN 0 340 77539 4.

First published 2000

Impression number 10 9 8 7 6 5 4
Year   2004 2003 2002 2001

Front cover images from Ronald Grant and Corbis.

Produced by Gray Publishing, Tunbridge Wells, Kent.
Printed in Great Britain for Hodder & Stoughton Educational, a division of Hodder Headline Plc, 338 Euston Road, London NW1 3BH by The Bath Press, Bath

Contents

AREA 3 SOCIETY, POLITICS AND THE ECONOMY — 139

APPENDICES — 211

INDEX — 239

GENERAL STUDIES

Acknowledgements

The publisher would like to thank the following for permission to reproduce the following copyright illustrations in this book:

AFP/Corbis page 106; Alex Bartel/Science Photo Library page 102; Bettmann/Corbis pages 7, 18, 45, 85, 131; Birkbeck College page 70; The Bridgeman Art Library page 79; CAMR/A.B. Dowsett/Science Photo Library page 37; National Statistics © Crown Copyright 2000 page 145; Image Sans Frontiers page 170; Chris Knapton/Science Photo Library page 59; NIBSC/Science Photo Library page 65; PA News Photo Library pages 96, 112, 187 and 192; Popperfoto pages 20, 137, 163, 197 and 209; Quest/Science Photo Library page 37; Science Photo Library page 13; Vanessa Vick/Science Photo Library page 34.

Every effort has been made to trace and acknowledge the ownership of copyright. The publisher will be glad to make any suitable arrangement with copyright holders whom it has not been possible to contact.

The specimen exam questions provided at the end of each chapter reflect topics set by each of the major awarding bodies (AQA, Edexcel and OCR) in previous General Studies examinations or in the specimen papers for the new AS and A levels.

Preface

How to use this book for the different specifications

All the specifications require you to study the Introduction. Identify which papers you are doing for which board and use the information below to tell you the issues that you need to study.

AQA specification A

Paper	Issues
AS Unit 1 Culture, morality, arts and humanities	12–14, 18–22
AS Unit 2 Science, mathematics and technology	1–9
A2 Unit 3W & 3C Society, politics and the economy	15–17, 23–24
A2 Unit 4 Culture, morality, arts and humanities	12–14, 18–22
A2 Unit 5 Science, mathematics and technology	1–11
A2 Unit 6 Society, politics and the economy	1–11, 14–17, 23–34

AQA specification B

Paper	Issues
AS Unit 1 Conflict	1, 5–8, 11, 19–20, 22–25, 31–32
AS Unit 2 Power	5, 7–8, 11–14, 18–22, 26, 28–30
AS Unit 3W Space	4–9, 15, 18, 21–22, 24, 27–28, 32–34
A2 Unit 4W & 4C Conflict resolution	1–3, 5, 12–13, 15, 18–24, 27–29, 31–34
A2 Unit 5 Power regulation	1–3, 5–11, 14–15, 19–22, 25–30, 31–34
A2 Unit 6 Space–Time	1–3, 7, 9–15, 18–24, 28–29, 34

Edexcel

Paper	Issues
AS Unit 1 Aspects of culture	12–14, 19, 20–22
AS Unit 2 Scientific horizons	1, 3, 6, 9–11, 22
AS Unit 3a & b Social perspectives	4, 23–24, 27, 29–30, 32–33
A2 Unit 4a & b Cultural expressions	2, 6, 13–14, 18–19, 21–22
A2 Unit 5 Modern society	14, 23, 25, 27–30, 33
A2 Unit 6 The contemporary world	1–3, 5–6, 9–11, 14–15, 20, 22–24, 29–34

OCR

Paper	Issues
AS Unit 1 The cultural domain	14–15, 19–20, 22–24, 28–29
AS Units 2 & 3 The scientific domain	3–9, 24
AS Unit 4 The social domain	7, 22–24, 26, 29, 31–33
A2 Unit 5 The scientific and cultural domains	1–3, 5–11, 12–14, 18–21
A2 Units 6 & 7 The social domain	15–17, 23–28, 31–33
A2 Unit 8 Culture, science and society: making connections	All the issues

Introduction

All the General Studies syllabuses/specifications require candidates to display thinking and analytical skills in every area of the specification. Furthermore, 25% of the marks in the examinations are given for AO4 (Assessment Objective 4) (demonstrate understanding of different types of knowledge and of the relationships between them, appreciating their limitations). Therefore it is essential that you should understand exactly what this means, and how you can develop and use these skills to answer the types of questions you may be set.

Types of knowledge

You may be required to identify different types of knowledge and show that you understand what makes them different from each other.

Scientific knowledge

This is knowledge based on observation and experimentation. For example, photosynthesis is scientific knowledge because it is based on observation of plant growth followed by experimentation to show that energy from the sun combines carbon dioxide and water to produce glucose (see Figure 1). So if you can identify a type of knowledge based on the type of method described in Issue 3 (Scientific knowledge and its application), it is scientific knowledge.

Objective knowledge

This is knowledge based on facts upon which everyone would agree, regardless of their feelings. Scientific knowledge is a form of objective knowledge but so are facts such as, 'The Times is a daily newspaper owned by Rupert Murdoch' or 'England won the FIFA World Cup in 1966'. The opposite of objective knowledge is subjective knowledge.

Figure 1 The principles of photosynthesis

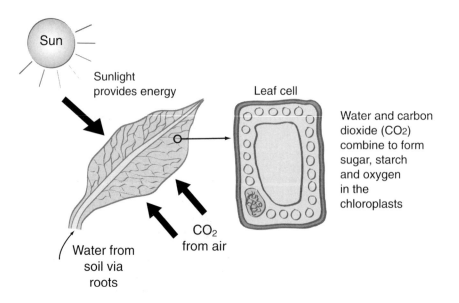

Sun

Sunlight provides energy

Leaf cell

Water and carbon dioxide (CO_2) combine to form sugar, starch and oxygen in the chloroplasts

CO_2 from air

Water from soil via roots

GENERAL STUDIES

Subjective knowledge

This is knowledge based on a person's feelings or beliefs and so would not be agreed upon by everyone. Examples of subjective knowledge are statements such as, 'Oasis are the best musicians in the world', 'Scientists should not let their feelings affect their science', 'New Labour has abandoned socialism'.

Knowledge based on belief

This is closely connected with subjective knowledge. It is something that is thought to be true, but which has not been proven in the same way as scientific knowledge, or accepted as factual like objective knowledge. Things can be believed to be true because of the evidence of other people; for example, if I say someone owns a pig because my friend has told me, this is knowledge based on belief, as my friend may be lying or mistaken. Things can be believed to be true because they are thought to be the best explanation of the facts; for example, someone might believe in the existence of God because it makes sense of their life. Knowledge based on belief can also be called opinion.

Knowledge based on moral values

This is knowledge based on what is considered right or wrong. A person's moral values are those that a person believes are the guiding principles in life; they may be religious or a concept such as utilitarianism (see Issue 13, 'Why people have religious belief'). Examples of knowledge based on moral values are statements such as, '*Pulp Fiction* is a bad film because it demeans women' or 'Multinational companies cheat the Third World' (see Figure 2).

Figure 2 Types of knowledge

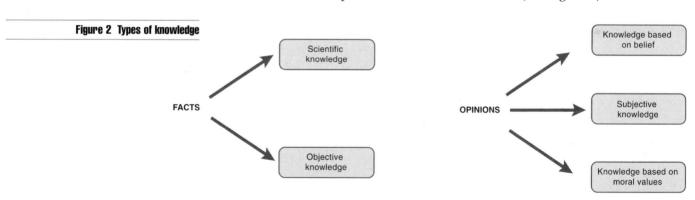

Types of argument

A deductive argument

This is one where the conclusion can be deduced from the premises, i.e. it follows automatically. It argues from the general to the particular. For example, if the angles of a triangle equal 180 degrees (general statement), and in a particular triangle two angles equal 120 degrees, you can deduce that the other must equal 60 degrees.

Any deductive argument will be true, as long as the premises are true.

Did you know?

The gardener analogy

Two explorers come across a clearing in jungle. One of them says that the clearing must be the work of a gardener. The other disputes the claim and says there is no gardener. He suggests they sit and watch for the gardener, but the first explorer says that the gardener is probably invisible. The second explorer points to the weeds in the clearing as evidence that there is no gardener, but the first explorer claims that the gardener has left them because he likes weeds.

Several philosophers have used the analogy to illustrate the problem of arguing from lack of evidence and how an argument is invalid if it cannot be falsified.

An inductive argument

This is one that argues from the particular to the general. It usually argues from a group of particular experiences in the world to a general conclusion. For example, I have made 2000 experiments on boiling water and in each one the water boiled at 100°C, therefore water always boils at 100°C.

Any inductive argument will only be probable because it is based on experience, and we can never be certain about experience. For example, you only need to boil water once on Mount Everest to realise that water does not always boil at 100°C.

However, some inductive arguments are better than others, depending on the amount and reliability of evidence and the predictability of it happening again. For example, it is more certain that a liquid will turn to a gas if you apply sufficient heat (scientific law) than that an unemployed Protestant male will commit suicide (sociological theory).

This is explored in more detail in Issue 3.

Arguing from authority

This is claiming that something is true because an important person or book says that it is, e.g. 'Murder is wrong because the Bible says so' or 'God exists because Einstein said he did'.

Arguing from authority is a weak form of argument unless the authority you quote is an authority that everyone recognises, e.g. 'Light does not travel in straight lines because Einstein said so'. To claim that God exists when your only evidence is that Einstein (whose authority is in science not religion) says so is not a valid form of argument. To claim that murder is wrong on the authority of the Bible is not a valid argument unless you show why the Bible has moral authority. This is a false argument unless you have given evidence to show that everything the Bible says is true.

Arguing to the person

This is claiming that something is false because the person who put it forward is a bad person (or true because the person who put it forward is a good person). This is a false argument because it is evidence alone that decides whether an argument is true or false.

Arguing from analogy

This is where someone quotes a similar case and argues from this that the same thing applies to a different situation. For example, William Paley argued that because a watch is a complex mechanism that could not have made been made by chance, the world, which is also a complex mechanism, could not have been made by chance either. However, for an argument from analogy to work, it must be shown that the two things are the same, i.e. that the world has all the order of a watch and the watch has all the disorder of the world.

Arguing from lack of evidence

This is claiming that something is true because there is no evidence to say it is false. For example, no one has ever proven that fairies do not exist, therefore they must exist. This is a false argument because there has to be evidence upon which to decide whether something is true or false.

Analysing arguments

All this knowledge of the nature of arguments should help you to analyse an argument. Analysing an argument means:

- identifying the main points of the argument
- deciding whether these points are based on knowledge or belief
- working out whether the argument is based on evidence or on the beliefs/opinions of the author
- identifying any bias in the argument
- deciding how valid the argument is.

How to decide whether an argument is valid or justified

A *valid argument* is either a deductive argument or an argument based on scientific or objective knowledge, where the conclusion or interpretation follows from the evidence and where the conclusion cannot be doubted.

A *justified argument* is an argument that has reasons; the reasons are factually correct and the conclusion or interpretation follows from the reasons, but is not the only possible conclusion. An example would be the film *Shakespeare in Love*, which interprets *Romeo and Juliet* as a product of Shakespeare falling in love; this is a justified argument, but it is not the only possible interpretation.

You may find the flowchart in Figure 3 useful in helping you to decide whether an argument is valid or justified.

Deciding whether or not something is true

Philosophers have argued for the past 100 years about what truth is – indeed, Pontius Pilate asked Jesus, 'What is truth?'. Some philosophers argue that the truth is what corresponds to the facts, e.g. the statement 'Swans are white' is true because it corresponds to the facts (this is known as the correspondence theory of truth). Others argue that what is true is what has not been falsified. It is not true to say that swans are white because Australian swans are black. However, it is true to say that most swans are white.

ACTIVITIES

① When the explorer in the gardener analogy says there is a gardener, is he arguing from knowledge or from belief?

② What would be the problems of someone who would not accept that any evidence could invalidate their argument?

③ Read the leader columns of some quality newspapers (e.g. The Times, The Guardian, The Independent). Analyse the arguments that are put forward using the method outlined in either the section on analysing arguments above or in the flow chart in Figure 3.

Figure 3 Is an argument valid?

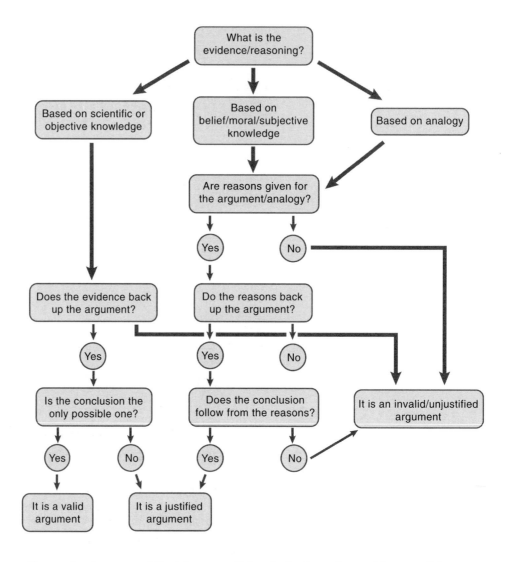

It can also be argued that for something to be true, it must be possible to show that it could be false. For example if you say, 'I have been to Australia', that is a possible true statement because there are ways in which I could prove your statement false. However, if I say, 'I have an invisible, odourless, inaudible, tasteless rabbit which you would not be able to feel if you touched it', my statement is not a possible true statement because there is no way you could show it to be false.

As far as you are concerned for the exam, if you think of truth as that which fits the facts and could be shown to be false, this will be enough to enable you to show the difference between knowledge and belief.

Area...1

SCIENCE, MATHEMATICS AND TECHNOLOGY

1

Scientific progress

In order to decide how scientific progress has been made, it is necessary to define what is meant by science.

The *Oxford English Dictionary* defines science as 'a branch of knowledge conducted on objective principles involving the systemized observation of and experiment with phenomena, especially concerned with the material and functions of the physical universe'.

This could be further defined as:

- observing regularities in nature, e.g. the way in which the seasons follow each other
- working out a rational theory to explain why these regularities happen, e.g. that the earth moves round the sun tilted at an angle and the seasons change as the earth leans towards or away from the sun
- formulating the theory into a formula that predicts what will happen, e.g. when the North Pole is tilted 23.4 degrees towards the sun, the vertical noon rays are directly over the Tropic of Cancer.

Ideas about progress in science

Science has obviously made a lot of progress since the days when people thought that rain was caused by God opening windows in the firmament, but how has this change come about?

- The traditional theory is that science has grown gradually as scholars learned a little more in each successive generation and built on what they had learned from the previous generation.
- Another view is that progress in science depends on the nature of the society in which a scientist or scholar is living. If the society is changing rapidly or encourages people to think freely and to question traditional ideas, then there will be scientific progress. If a society is settled and has a system of authority where questioning traditions is punished, there will be little or no scientific progress (see Issue 11, 'The impact of science on culture').
- Some scientists believe that progress in science depends on technology (making tools and instruments). For example, scientists could not have made discoveries about the planets without telescopes (see Issue 11).
- In *The Structure of Scientific Revolutions* (1962) Thomas Kuhn, an American historian of science, suggested that scientific progress is made in sudden jumps. He argued that, in any society, scientists accept a paradigm given to them by their society. By a paradigm Kuhn meant a view of what the world is like, how it works and how it can be investigated. He argued that the paradigm tells scientists what is important in science, what questions to ask and what problems are important. Change only occurs when scientists discover problems and contradictions in the paradigm. Eventually this causes a crisis, resulting in a new paradigm. This sudden change of paradigms is like a revolution in science and brings about progress because new ideas are then needed.

In order for you to have sufficient information with which to answer a question on scientific progress, it is necessary to give a brief history of science.

A history of science

Early history

Archaeological evidence, such as cave paintings and scratches on bits of bone, indicates that humans have always been close observers of nature. Indeed, the whole of agriculture must be based on early humans observing the seasons and the way in which seeds grow in order to grow crops successfully. In the megalithic structures (such as Stonehenge) found in China, Central America, Mesopotamia, Egypt and Europe, there is evidence of knowledge of a number of mathematical principles, including that of the square on the hypotenuse equalling the sum of the squares on the other two sides in a right-angled triangle, almost 2000 years before Pythagoras.

Greek science

Euclid provided a mathematical basis for science by discovering the main theorems of geometry. Archimedes developed a method for manipulating scientific observations into a scientific law in mathematical terms, which can be used to predict what will happen in such discoveries as his laws on levers and the displacement of water.

Aristotle developed the view that science is concerned with observation followed by theorising by asking questions such as 'What is the form of the object or process being observed?', 'How did it get that form?' and 'What is its purpose?'. From these observations, Aristotle determined that the world is made up of four elements: earth, water, air and fire. Aristotle's view that the earth is the centre of the universe (the geocentric principle) was finalised by Ptolemy, who devised a system of small circles on top of larger ones that enabled astronomers to predict the movement of the sun and planets while assuming that the earth was stationary.

The great gift of the Greeks to science was their belief that the universe works on rational, natural laws discoverable by humans.

Medieval science

The Greek scientific ideas were developed in Islamic science, especially in medicine, and in the Arab discoveries of the number system, algebra and chemistry. This Islamic science and the works of Aristotle were rediscovered in Europe when Spain was recaptured from the Islamic Empire. The medieval scientists were concerned with technology, discovering such things as the crank and gears, which enabled them to harness wind and water power for the beginnings of industry. They also used experiments to help to discover the natural laws.

The rise of modern science

Copernicus challenged the basis of much early science in 1543 when he suggested that the earth goes round the sun. This heliocentric theory was backed up when the telescope was discovered and Galileo was able to show the

Did you know?

Light, rain and rainbows

Medieval scientists investigated the nature of light in a rainbow by simulating the conditions under which the rainbows occur. Hollow glass balls filled with water were substituted for raindrops and light was passed through them. Conclusions about the behaviour of light could then be drawn without the huge difficulty of waiting for a rainbow to appear.

phases of Venus and moons around Jupiter (1610). Galileo's experiments on motion also showed that Aristotle's ideas were false.

Other seventeenth-century scientists built on Galileo's use of experiments and close observation. William Harvey discovered the circulation of the blood in 1628. Robert Boyle made various discoveries in chemistry, most famously Boyle's law of the compressibility of gas in 1662. Isaac Newton discovered the principles of gravity and motion in 1687.

It is generally thought that the basic principles of science were finalised by Newton (see Issue 3, 'Scientific method and its application'), but there is much argument as to whether the Copernican Revolution (as many historians call the change from an earth-centred to a sun-centred system) was just a development of medieval science, the result of technology, or a new revolutionary idea.

You could use Issue 7 ('Transport issues'), Issue 8 ('Energy'), Issue 9 ('Developments in technology') or Issue 10 ('Medicine') to answer questions on scientific progress, but the subject of gravitational motion is a good way of doing so.

The progress of science as seen in gravitational motion

Early scientists did not realise that there was a connection between the way objects fall to earth and the motion of the stars and planets. Aristotle claimed that the heavenly bodies were divine and in eternal, unchanging motion. As far as objects on earth are concerned, they had a natural tendency to move towards the earth's centre. These ideas led to a theory of motion that a body moving at a constant speed must have a constant force acting on it directly (i.e. interaction at a distance was impossible).

These ideas seemed to fit the facts as they were known. Indeed, the heliocentric theory causes problems. Galileo was asked why bodies do not fly off the earth if it is spinning on its axis and circling the sun. He was also asked why an object dropped from a tower falls to the bottom of the tower when the earth has moved between it being dropped and it landing. Galileo's answer was that bodies do not fly off the earth because, in revolutions per minute, they are not travelling very fast. Objects dropped from a tower share the earth's rotation with the tower and so drop at the base of the tower. In his experiments of dropping objects, Galileo discovered that the distance a falling object travels varies as the square of the time.

Johannes Kepler (1571–1630) discovered that the planets move in ellipses rather than circles. He saw a great problem with planetary motion and suggested that the sun emitted a magnetic force, which pushed the planets around it.

It was Newton who realised that it is the same force that makes objects fall to the ground and that makes the planets move in elliptical orbits. His law of universal gravitation states that there is a force of attraction between any two bodies that is proportional to the inverse square of their separation and the

Figure 1.1 'The wonder is not that mankind comprehends the world, but that the world is comprehensible.' (Einstein)

product of their masses ($F = GmM/d^2$). This law explains why objects of differing weights fall to earth at the same speed and why planets have elliptical orbits.

Newton's laws were accepted until Einstein proposed that the elliptical paths of the planets were not caused by the gravitational effects of the sun, but because the presence of a gravitational field caused a curvature of space–time. In the general theory of relativity, Einstein explained why objects fall and how the whole universe operates. His theory is generally regarded as having been confirmed at the eclipse of 1919, when scientists could see that light travels in curves rather than straight lines, and by the red-shift effect in light (which is also evidence for the Big Bang). This evidence came after the theory, but Einstein's theory is based on the mathematics of Bernhard Riemann (1826–1866) about geodesics (the straightest curve possible in a curved grid). Some scientists also think that increased accuracy in telescopes showed that Newton's law was inaccurate in calculating Mercury's orbit before Einstein formulated his theory.

Specimen exam questions

AS   Choose any great scientist or inventor, briefly describe the science related to their discovery or invention, and assess its impact on society.

A2   What do you understand by 'scientific progress'? To what extent has the world benefited or failed to benefit from the exploitation of scientific knowledge and understanding?

① What is your paradigm?

② Use the Internet to discover the scientific principles involved in: the building of Stonehenge; Archimedes' law of levers; Archimedes and the displacement of water; a water mill; a windmill.

③ What do you understand by Einstein's quotation about the world being comprehensible?

2

Religion and science

As a working generalisation, it could be argued that science asks the question, 'Given that there is a world, *how* do things within it work?'. Religion tends to ask the question, '*Why* is there anything at all?'.

The nature of science

The modern age has often been described by historians and other thinkers as 'the age of science'. The value of science is that it provides us with accurate information about the world, which has been established by the most reliable methods available. Scientists produce an *hypothesis* – a starting point for future experiments and systematic observations which either confirm or refute the original assumption and then enable the observer to formulate a theory. This theory will be based on repeatability – the fact that the experiment has been repeated endlessly and produced the same result given identical conditions – and predictability – the extremely high probability that the same result will occur in the future.

Science is useful because it helps us to explain and formulate rules about the way the physical world works and to control, adapt and survive in it, for example by:

- producing a theory to explain tides in sea and rivers;
- designing a steel bridge that will successfully cope with any future loads;
- discovering that cyanide is poisonous to human beings.

The nature of religion

Religion can be defined as 'a particular system of faith and worship, usually involving recognition of a superhuman controlling power, such as a personal God or Gods entitled to obedience and worship'. Unlike science, which is based on the *empirical* view that real knowledge comes to us by experience (i.e. via the senses), religion tends to claim that its knowledge comes from three sources:

- *Natural theology*. This is the view (particularly strong in the Roman Catholic tradition) that by the use of human reason, you can argue from evidence within the world to the existence of God.

  An example is the design argument, which was very popular during the eighteenth and nineteenth centuries. The complexities of a human eye or a butterfly's wing suggest a designer in the same way that the complexities of the world as a whole suggest a divine designer, rather than randomness.
- *Revealed theology*. God has revealed knowledge about himself to human beings through special writings such as the Bible or the Qu'ran, through special creeds passed on by the Church or other religious institutions or through special people, such as Jesus of Nazareth or the Prophet Muhammad.
- *Personal or mystical experience*. Human beings can have intensely personal experiences of the divine, which may drastically change their lives and their understanding of the world.

Creationism the view that the 'Genesis' creation accounts are compatible with scientific evidence and are as equally valid as the theory of evolution

Fundamentalism the view that the Bible is entirely true and divinely inspired

General relativity the theory of Albert Einstein that time, space, mass and energy are related to one another so that space and time are affected by gravity

Natural theology the view that human beings can find evidence in the physical world to establish the existence of God

Quantum physics the study of the way in which sub-atomic particles behave

The relationship between science and religion

Generally speaking, in the medieval period in the Western world, it was assumed that all knowledge would lead to God, who had created the world and whose mighty acts were described in the Bible. Knowledge was based on reason, authority and tradition.

- *Reason*. In general, this meant that which could be worked out by argument and logic, although Thomas Aquinas, the thirteenth-century theologian, also included evidence from the real world.
- *Authority*. This meant the church's spiritual authority headed by the Pope.
- *Tradition*. This meant what had always been believed and taught by the Church and what was contained in ancient writings, for example, Aristotle's view of the universe, which was accepted by the Church.

Development of science and the modern outlook

In the Middle Ages, no philosophers or theologians would have imagined that the conclusions of faith and reason could diverge. What you could find out for yourself – *reason* – and what you believed – *faith* – both came to the same conclusion. In addition, there was what God might reveal to you, which was to be accepted even if you did not understand it. However, after the cultural developments of the *Renaissance*, which started in the fifteenth century, the growth of scientific method transformed what we know and our views about how we acquire knowledge. There was a fundamental shift from a God-centred world towards a human-centered one. Humans became the measure of all things. Eventually, this led to a divergence between scientific knowledge and the traditional teaching of the church.

Period of transition

The seventeenth, eighteenth and early nineteenth centuries could be described as a transitional period. Most early scientists never doubted that their scientific examination of the world would reveal evidence of design, law and order, which would reinforce their belief in God as creator. Many sixteenth- and seventeenth-century thinkers, such as *Galileo*, *Descartes* and *Isaac Newton*, combined their belief in scientific method with more traditional beliefs. When Newton could not account mathematically for the irregular orbits of some of the planets, for example, he attributed their paths to the work of God.

Examples of conflict between science and religion

The trial of Galileo

Galileo has been described as the first scientist in the modern sense. In 1610, after his own observations using a telescope, Galileo published *The Message of the Stars*, in which he argued that the earth went round the sun, rather than the other way round. This view was condemned by the Church on the grounds that it contradicted the 'revealed truth' of scripture and the official church view, based on Aristotle. But in 1632, Galileo supported the earlier astronomer, Copernicus, who had also argued that the sun was the centre of the universe round which the planets revolved. Galileo was put on trial in 1633 and forced to withdraw his views by the Pope because he supported Copernicus's theory as a scientific fact, not just as a hypothesis. Galileo challenged the authority of established religion because:

• he based knowledge on the evidence of his senses – a modern empirical view;
• he claimed that the universe can be explained in terms of mathematical principles and in terms of cause and effect (Galileo himself, thought that God could be seen both in the 'book of nature' and in the 'book of scripture' – they were complementary, rather than in conflict).

Charles Darwin and evolution

In 1859, based on his long research, including 5 years spent on *HMS Beagle* as a naturalist, Darwin published *On the Origin of Species*, in which he put forward several radical theories.

• Different species have evolved from one common ancestry.
• *Natural selection*. Natural genetic mutation produces some characteristics that help some species to survive better than others and they pass on these favourable characteristics to future generations over a very long period of time. Less favourable characteristics cause some species to die out.
• Human beings have evolved from earlier species, such as apes.

Darwin's theory, despite its imperfections, makes a fundamental contribution to the scientific view of the world. But it was furiously opposed at the time by many traditional religious believers, supported by others and criticised by some contemporary scientists. Darwin challenged the traditional views that:

• the world was created in 4004 BCE;
• each species had been created separately by God and was distinct;
• human beings were specially created by God and were different from other animals;
• the Genesis creation myths were a true historical account of how the world started.

 **Did you know?**

Scientific thoughts

Copernicus (1473–1543), a Polish priest, published his main work on the movement of heavenly bodies in 1543. He argued that the sun is at the centre of the universe and that the earth revolves around it once a year.

The *Heisenberg uncertainty principle* argues that it is impossible to know for certain both the position and the momentum of an electron at the same time. This appears to attack the view that science can explain and predict the behaviour of material objects exactly.

Evidence for evolution is strongly suggested by the fact that 99% of a chimpanzee's genetic material is the same as that of a human.

Is it possible to believe in science and religion in the twenty-first century?

Some modern thinkers have suggested that the contrast between scientific thinking and religious thinking is not as great as has been claimed, and, indeed, that science still leads to God.

It is not true that everything is certain in science. In physics, light is sometimes described as waves, sometimes as particles. At one stage, the Newtonian view of fixed space and time was regarded as scientific fact, but now Einstein's theory of relativity, which argues that space and time can be affected by gravity, holds sway. In quantum physics, the behaviour of sub-atomic particles can only be predicted with probability, rather than certainty. At this level, scientists need the same powers of imagination, creativity and the ability to trust their judgement, which characterises religious belief.

Figure 2.1 'Two things never fail to fill me with awe, the starry heavens above the earth and the moral world within.' (Immanuel Kant)

① Recently, a county school board in America banned the teaching of evolutionary theory in their school because it contradicted their Creationist views. How far do you think this action can be justified?

② Is 'Where did the world come from?' a scientific or a religious question and why?

The philosopher, Ludwig Wittgenstein, argued that we need to understand the context in which language is used in order to discover its meaning. Scientific language and religious language serve different purposes, and both are equally valid in their own situation. Religion asks questions such as, 'Who am I?' or 'What is the meaning of life?'. Like general scientific theories (such as relativity), these questions are looking for truths that affect our lives, and they can be discussed rationally, but they produce answers that cannot be observed by the senses. This implies that science and religion are ways of looking at life that should be seen as complementary to each other, rather than in conflict.

Some scientists argue that the evidence for the Big Bang and evolution is also evidence for the existence of God. The fact that if the Big Bang had been a microsecond earlier the universe would have imploded and a microsecond later and it would have exploded so fast that everything would have disappeared implies that God determined the moment of the Big Bang. Some scientists also argue for the anthropic principle (that at the moment of the Big Bang the nature of matter, the size of the bang and the laws of science made it inevitable that humans would be created) as evidence of God using science to create humans. Other scientists claim that the scientific coincidences necessary for life on earth (stars being made out of hydrogen and helium to produce carbon and supernovae being needed to spread the carbon to planets like earth) are so great that it could not have happened by chance, and so God must have caused it.

Some religious philosophers argue that the way we live our lives (and especially the way in which scientists conduct science) is based on the principle that everything has an explanation. The search for explanations has worked well in science and if everything in the universe has an explanation, it seems reasonable to accept that the universe itself must have an explanation. The only being who could explain the universe would be God, therefore it is reasonable to believe that God exists.

Specimen exam questions

AS To what extent do you think that the discoveries and theories of Charles Darwin in the nineteenth century have contributed to the decline in religious belief in the twentieth century?

A2 'It is not possible to believe in *both* science *and* religion in the twenty-first century.' Evaluate the arguments for and against this view.

3

Scientific method and its application

Science is concerned with the phenomena of the universe, i.e. the physical things that happen in the universe. The methods used by scientists to explore the phenomena and come up with laws or theories to explain them are known as scientific method.

The scientific method

A seventeenth-century English scientist, Francis Bacon, worked out a formal method of scientific investigation based on studying empirical evidence ('empirical' means evidence that can be tested by the senses). This has been developed into the method that you probably use for GCSE science coursework (see Figure 3.1).

All of science has to be *inductive* rather than *deductive* because it argues from a set of particular observations to a general law. However, what makes it scientific is that it is difficult to reject the conclusion without being irrational, and, more particularly, the experiments can always be repeated and will have the same conclusion (this is often called predictability – science can predict what will happen).

Figure 3.1 The scientific method

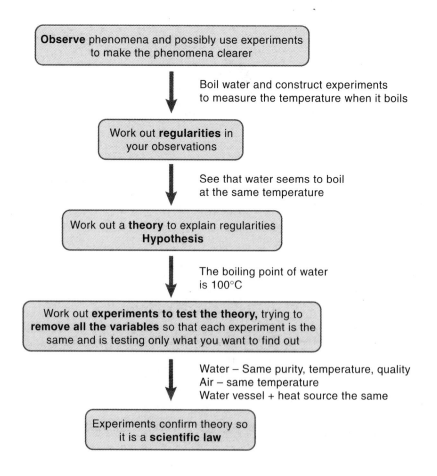

Observe phenomena and possibly use experiments to make the phenomena clearer

Boil water and construct experiments to measure the temperature when it boils

Work out **regularities** in your observations

See that water seems to boil at the same temperature

Work out a **theory** to explain regularities **Hypothesis**

The boiling point of water is 100°C

Work out **experiments to test the theory,** trying to **remove all the variables** so that each experiment is the same and is testing only what you want to find out

Water – Same purity, temperature, quality
Air – same temperature
Water vessel + heat source the same

Experiments confirm theory so it is a **scientific law**

Some philosophers of science follow Karl Popper and claim that the scientific method is based on *falsifying* rather than *verifying* ('verifying' – the use of scientific experiment to test whether a theory is true). They claim that science makes progress as scientists test theories or laws and find areas where they are false. Then they amend the law or theory to fit the new evidence (e.g. changing the air pressure and discovering that water does not always boil at 100°C and then devising the law that water boils at 100°C minus 1°C for every 300 m above sea level).

Using scientific method

The crucial points when trying to apply scientific method to any issue are to:

- use evidence that can be tested by the senses;
- work out a theory to explain the evidence;
- work out tests of the theory (experiments) that reduce the number of variables to as few as possible;
- decide whether the tests have given enough evidence to say that the theory is valid (true beyond reasonable doubt).

The application of scientific method – evolution

Some scientists would regard the most important theory in the biological sciences as evolutionary theory. Evolution means gradual change over the course of time and the theory is that life on earth has evolved over 3–4 billion years from very simple to very complex organisms, through modifications in each generation.

Observations

Naturalists such as Linnaeus (the first person to classify plants) and Lamarck had observed similarities between species in the eighteenth century. Linnaeus proposed that species could change, and Lamarck devised an evolutionary tree from tiny animals to human beings. Technological advances in canal and road building led to geological discoveries and fossils that seemed to show gradually changing life forms.

Charles Darwin, on his voyage to the Galápagos Islands on *HMS Beagle*, observed differences between species living on neighbouring islands and a similarity between living creatures and fossil remains in the same area.

The theory

In his *On the Origin of Species* (1859), Darwin proposed that life on earth has evolved from the very simple forms of life seen in the earliest fossils to complex mammals such as humans through 'natural selection'. In each generation more offspring are produced than can survive and some of the offspring have slight variations; the forces of nature (restricted food supply, disease, predators, etc.) destroy those less adapted to survive and those that do survive will pass on their successful variation to the next generation, so that over long periods of time, major changes will occur.

Did you know?

SI units

SI units the international system of units of measurement (from the French Système Internationale)

Kilogram the SI unit of mass

Metre the SI unit of length

Second the SI unit of time

Ampère the SI unit of electric current

Kelvin the SI unit of temperature

Mole the SI unit of the quantity of a substance (number of particles, rather than mass)

Candela the SI unit of intensity of light

Newton the SI unit of force

Joule the SI unit of work

Watt the SI unit of power

Pascal the SI unit of pressure

Hertz the SI unit of frequency

Coulomb the SI unit of electric charge

Volt the SI unit of potential difference

Farad the SI unit of capacitance

Ohm the SI unit of resistance

Figure 3.2 Charles Darwin

The evidence

Since Darwin's time, much testing of the fossil record as been possible (see Figure 3.2).

Discoveries in DNA have shown that the history of evolution is stored in the gene strands of DNA, and molecular biology is now able to trace some parts of the evolutionary process.

Conclusion

Scientists regard evolution in terms of organisms being related by common descent as a fact. There is so much evidence that it is irrational to doubt it. What is still regarded as theory is *why* evolution occurs.

The application of scientific method – plate tectonics

Some scientists would regard the most important theory in the earth sciences as plate tectonics. This is a recent theory, which has been as revolutionary for earth sciences as Copernicus was for astronomy and physics. It claims that all the geological processes of the earth – mountains, oceans, volcanoes, earthquakes, etc. can be explained by the structure and behaviour of a small number of huge rigid plates, which form the outer part of the planet earth (known as the lithosphere).

Observations

In 1911, Alfred Wegener claimed that observation of the early geological history of the earth showed that there was once only one continent (which he named Pangaea). This was modified by du Toit in 1937 to the existence of two continents. Both these scientists had observed that the fossils in the pre-Cretaceous rock strata of Africa and South America (over 140 million years old) and the pre-Jurassic rocks of India, Australia, Madagascar and Africa (over 200 million years old) are so similar that they appear once to have been part of the same land mass.

In the 1950s it was observed that the magnetised remains in rocks indicate that the magnetic poles were at different places on the earth at different periods in the earth's history.

The theory

In the mid-1960s, the Canadian geologist Tuzo Wilson suggested that the regularities of the observations could be explained if the earth's crust were made up of plates much thicker than the continents and the ocean floors. These plates cover the whole surface of the earth, but where they meet each other, the nature of the plates either results in one plate going lower (creating oceans) or a collision (creating mountain ranges). Where two plates pass each other without subduction (one going lower) or collision, there is a fracture zone (e.g. the San Andreas Fault in California). Wilson claimed that most of the earth's seismic activity occurs along plate boundaries.

The evidence

Drilling of the ocean floors in the 1970s and 1980s confirmed that the ocean floors are less than 200 million years old, whereas the earth itself is around 4.5 billion years old.

Computer graphics have shown that at about 1000 m depth, the continents do match each other.

Isotopic dating has shown that the pre-Cambrian rocks in Africa and South America are the same in age and composition.

Figure 3.3 Continental distribution 80 million years ago

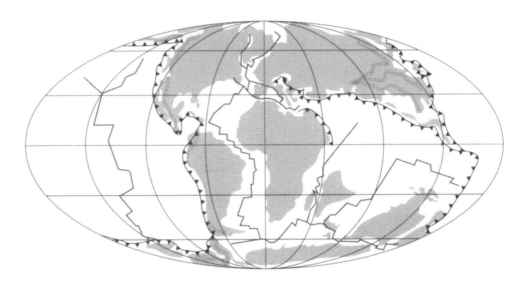

Conclusion

Plate tectonics is still a theory rather than a fact because there are some pieces of evidence that do not fit the theory (e.g. the Rocky Mountains of North America cannot be explained by plate collision). However, the theory does seem to work and scientists are using the method suggested by Popper to adapt the theory to cover the exceptions.

Figure 3.4 Science fact or science fiction?

ACTIVITIES

① Look at the photo in Figure 3.4 and try to formulate a theory to explain the phenomena of people seeing UFOs.

Work out some experiments to test your theory and explain what would be needed for scientific proof of the existence of UFOs.

Specimen exam questions

AS It has been claimed that left-handed people are more skilful at sports requiring hand–eye coordination than right-handed people. Explain how you would test this theory scientifically and how you would present your results.

A2 Discuss ways in which you could utilise everyday items and situations in the home to convey a basic understanding of two of the following scientific concepts: force; energy; life; metal.

4

The application of maths

Most of the maths in General Studies is the maths you need for Key Skills Level 3 numeracy, which is mainly concerned with interpreting statistics and tables and probability. This unit gives you some of the basic techniques you will need to do this. It would be a good idea to practise some GCSE Intermediate or Higher Maths papers to brush up your maths skills.

Mean, median, mode and range

The following were the scores in a golf tournament: 72, 86, 67, 94, 76, 82, 76, 69, 74, 76.

You find the *mean (average)* for the golf scores by adding together all the figures and dividing by the number of figures. This is 770 divided by 10 (the number of scores), giving a mean of 77. If you are given a table of statistics that gives the frequency of classes, you find the mid-value of each class (by halving it) and multiply by the frequency, add all those results together and divide by the number in the sample (see Table 4.1).

You find the *median* by putting the numbers into order of size, dividing the number of figures by 2 (essentially the middle value) and the median is the middle number. The golf scores put into order of size are: 67, 69, 72, 74, 76, 76, 76, 82, 86, 94. The fifth number is the middle number, so the median is 76.

The *mode* is the figure that occurs most frequently. In the golf scores, 76 occurs three times, but all the others only occur once, so the mode is 76. Sometimes a question will ask for the modal group rather than the mode, but it means the same.

The *range* is the difference between the lowest number and the highest number. In the golf scores, the highest number is 94, the lowest is 67, so the range is 27. Often you will need to find the interquartile range on a cumulative frequency graph (a graph where the frequencies of a statistics are added together as you go along). You do this by dividing the frequencies by 4 and plotting one-quarter and three-quarters. The interquartile range is the range between these (see Figure 4.1).

There are some ideas you need to know about when interpreting these concepts. The bigger the range (especially the interquartile range), the more unreliable the mean is likely to be. If the range is large, the median is likely to be a more reliable figure than the mean. If the range is small, the mean is the most reliable figure. Interpreting statistics also requires you to think about who is using the figures and what they want them for, e.g. a shoe manufacturer will be more interested in the mode of shoe sizes than the mean (they will need to gear their production of shoes to the popularity of sizes).

Table 4.1 illustrates the distance between home and the town centre of a group of 75 students and how to work out the mean distance.

Figure 4.1 illustrates how to draw a cumulative frequency graph and calculate the interquartile range using the figures from Table 4.1.

Distance in km (d)	No. of students (frequency, f)	Mid-interval value (MIV)	f × MIV
1 km or less	6	0.5	3.0
1 < d ≤ 2	7	1.5	10.5
2 < d ≤ 3	15	2.5	37.5
3 < d ≤ 4	18	3.5	63.0
4 < d ≤ 5	10	4.5	45.0
5 < d ≤ 6	10	5.5	55.0
6 < d ≤ 7	7	6.5	45.5
7 < d ≤ 8	2	7.5	15.0
Total	75		274.5

Mean = 274.5 (mid-interval value frequency added together) ÷ 75 (total no. in sample) = 3.66 km.

Table 4.1 *Mean distance between home and town centre for a group of 75 students (km)*

Figure 4.1 Cumulative frequency and calculation of the interquartile range

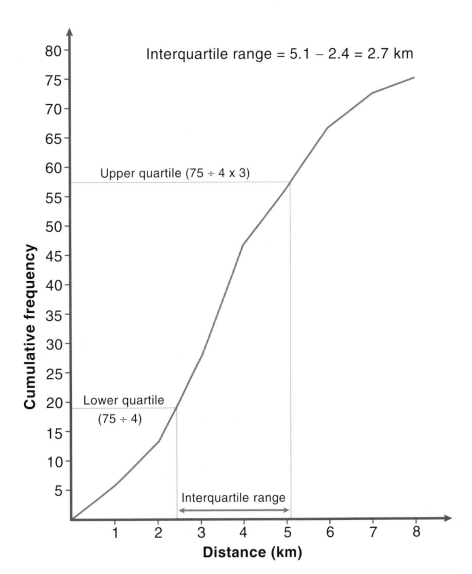

Interquartile range = 5.1 − 2.4 = 2.7 km

Upper quartile (75 ÷ 4 x 3)

Lower quartile (75 ÷ 4)

Interquartile range

Cumulative frequency

Distance (km)

Scatter graphs

A scatter graph is a graph that simply records a set of results without putting them into classes or groups. If you can draw a line of best fit through the results, there is a correlation in the results. The *line of best fit* is a straight line that is closest to the majority of points on the graph. If the line of best fit goes up, there is a *positive correlation* (if one variable rises, the other does as well). If the line of fit goes down, there is a *negative correlation* (if one variable goes up, the other will go down). If you cannot draw a line of best fit, there is no correlation.

Lines of best fit can be used to predict what will happen on the other variable (see Figure 4.2).

Figure 4.2 Lines of best fit

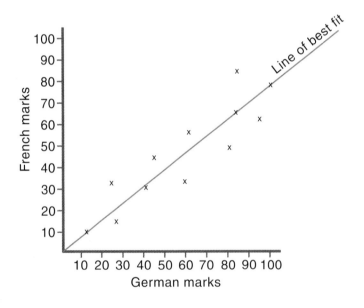

This means that if someone scores 50 in German, they are likely to score 40 in French

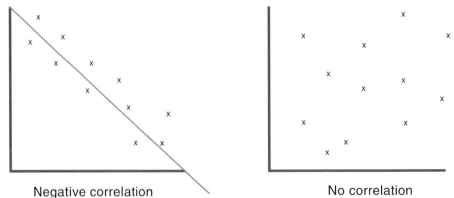

Negative correlation   No correlation

SCIENCE, MATHEMATICS AND TECHNOLOGY

Calculating percentages

1 You are likely to be asked what percentage is represented by one of the figures in the tables. To do this, you work out the total number, then apply the formula:

$$\frac{(\text{figure you need} \times 100)}{\text{total number}}$$

For example, the percentage of golfers scoring 76 is: $\dfrac{3 \times 100}{10} = 30\%$

2 You may be asked to find a percentage difference. To do this, you work out the difference, multiply by 100 and divide by the original amount.

For example, a shopkeeper buys soap powder at £10 for five packets and sells it for £2.75 per packet. What is his percentage profit?

$$1000 \div 5 = 200 \text{ (the amount he pays for one packet)},$$
$$275 - 200 = 75 \text{ (the profit per packet)} \times 100 \div 200 = 37.5\%.$$

3 You may be asked to remove part of a percentage. To do this, you add the percentage you have to remove to 100, divide by the total and multiply by 100.

For example, if a computer costs £1175 including 17.5% VAT, what would be its price without VAT?

$$100 + 17.5 = 117.5; \quad 1175 \div 117.5 \times 100 = £1000.$$

4 You may be asked to find an original amount when a percentage has been taken off. To do this, you subtract that percentage from 100, divide the current amount by your answer and multiply by 100.

For example, a Playstation costs £76 in a 20% off sale. What was its price before the sale?

$$100 - 20 = 80; \quad 76 \div 80 \times 100 = £95.$$

5 You may be asked to work out compound interest. To do this, you add 100 to the annual interest, divide by 100 and store this in the memory of your calculator, then multiply by the capital (amount invested). You then keep multiplying by the stored number for the number of years of interest.

For example, what would £5000 be worth after 5 years if invested at compound interest of 6.5% per annum?

This is what you do on your calculator:

100 + 6.5 ÷ 100 STO M+ × 5000 × RCL M+ × RCL M+ × RCL M+ RCL M+ = £6850.43.

If you are asked for the amount of interest, you simply subtract the amount invested from your calculator answer.

KEY words

Cubics an equation where the highest power is 3. You solve a cubic equation by drawing a graph and finding the values of x from where the line crosses the x-axis (there are three answers)

Exponential change growth at regular intervals, which can be calculated in the same way as compound interest

Gradient how far a line goes up in ratio to how far it goes along. To find the gradient, you divide up by along. A downward gradient will be a negative number

Histogram a bar chart with the width of the columns in proportion to the size of the group, the vertical axis based on frequency density (frequency divided by the class interval) so that the area of the column represents the frequency

Networks often called critical path analysis, requiring you to work out which activities are connected and which activities depend on a previous activity and then link them together into a network

Did you know?

Re-arranging formulae

Re-arranging formulae allows you to work out the value of any missing figure in a formula. The basic rule for re-arranging formulae is that you move the letters to the opposite side of the equals sign until the letter you want is the subject of the formula. Every time you move a letter across the equals sign, you change its sign (change sides, change sign). This means that the minus changes to plus and plus to minus. Multiply changes to divide, and divide changes to multiply. Square changes to square root, square root to square. Cube changes to cube root, cube root to cube. It is a good idea to work out the order of importance of the signs in the formula so that you change the signs that apply to several letters first.

The formula for the volume of a sphere is:

$$V = \tfrac{4}{3}\pi r^3$$

What is the diameter of a football whose volume is 4189.33 cm³?

$$V = \tfrac{4}{3}\pi r^3$$

$$\frac{V}{\tfrac{4}{3}\pi} = r^3$$

$$\sqrt[3]{\frac{V}{\tfrac{4}{3}\pi}} = r$$

$$\sqrt[3]{\frac{4189.33}{\tfrac{4}{3}\pi}} = 10.$$

Diameter = 20 cm.

6 If you are asked to calculate depreciation, it is a very similar calculation to compound interest. You subtract the percentage depreciation from 100 and divide the answer by 100, store this in the memory, multiply by the initial value, then multiply by the stored number for every year of depreciation.

For example, if a car bought for £15 000 depreciates at 10% a year, what will its value be after 5 years?

This is what you do on your calculator:

$$100 - 10 \div 100 \text{ STO M+} \times 15\,000 \times \text{RCL M+} \times \text{RCL M+}$$
$$\times \text{RCL M+} \times \text{RCL M+} = £8857.35.$$

Calculating probability

Any probability can be written as a decimal between 0 and 1 where 0 is impossible and 1 is certain.

You work out the probability by dividing the chance by the total.

For example, the probability of throwing a six when you throw a die is 1 in 6 (there are six numbers and only one six); $1 \div 6 = 0.17$ probability.

When you have two possible outcomes you multiply the relevant outcomes to find the probability.

For example, Rebecca has a 2 in 3 chance of winning the darts competition and a 3 in 4 chance of winning the dominoes competition. What is the probability of her winning both competitions?

$$2 \div 3 \times 3 \div 4 = 0.5.$$

What is the probability that Rebecca will win only one of the competitions?

She has a 2 in 3 chance of winning the darts and a 1 in 4 chance of not winning the dominoes; she has a 3 in 4 chance of winning the dominoes and a 1 in 3 chance of not winning the darts. So what are her chances of only winning one event?

What you put into your calculator:

$$(2 \div 3 \times 1 \div 4) + (3 \div 4 \times 1 \div 3) = 0.4167.$$

Calculating volumes

The basic formula for calculating volume is height × length × width.

However, prisms cause problems because the volume is the area of the cross-section multiplied by the length.

The *volume of a cylindrical prism* is worked out by multiplying the area of the circle at the end of the cylinder by the height of the cylinder:

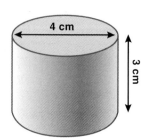

4 cm

3 cm

① In a sale a shop reduced all its prices by 15%.
(a) Find the new price of an article that originally cost £55.00.
(b) Find the original price of an article whose reduced price is £102.
(c) In the week before the sale, the average number of customers per day was 250. During the sale, this number increased to 370. What was the percentage increase?

② The ages of the members of a sports club were: less than 10 years, 2; 11–20 years, 16; 21–30 years, 30; 31–40 years, 16; 41–50 years, 10; over 50 years, 6.
(a) Draw a cumulative frequency graph and use it to find the median and interquartile range.
(b) State the modal group and estimate the mean.

③ Scarlett Rousers and Grace Ox make clothes together. The probability of Scarlett producing a sub-standard item is 0.1 and the probability of Grace producing a sub-standard item is 0.3.
(a) What is the probability that they will both produce a sub-standard item?
(b) In a consignment of 900 garments produced by them both, how many will have flaws?

④ A firm wants to start manufacturing televisions. This involves the following activities:
(a) order components; (b) order packing; (c) manufacture parts; (d) set up testing procedures;
(e) assemble sets; (f) test sets; (g) pack sets; (h) despatch sets to the wholesaler.
Draw a critical path network for this process.

Volume = 2 × 2 (radius squared) × π × 3 = 37.699 cm³ (cubic centimetres).

This means that, if you are given the volume and radius, you can work out the depth.

For example, how deep is the water in a cylinder of diameter 4 cm if there is 37.699 ml of water in the cylinder?

$$37.699 \div (2 \times 2 \times \pi) = 3 \text{ cm, so the depth is 3 cm}$$
$$(1 \text{ ml} = 1 \text{ cm}^3 \text{ and } 1000 \text{ cm}^3 = 1 \text{ litre}).$$

The *volume of a triangular prism* is worked out by finding the area of the cross-section triangle and multiplying by the length.

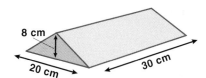

Volume = 10 × 8 (half the base of the triangle multiplied by the height to get the area of the triangle) × 30 (the length) = 2400 cm³.

Mass is the weight of an object, *density* is the weight per item of length.

$$Mass = \text{volume density};$$
$$Density = \text{mass volume};$$
$$Volume = \text{mass density}.$$

Specimen exam questions

Work through the appropriate specimen questions from the examination board whose General Studies and/or Key Skills papers you are taking.

5

Environmental issues

Environmental issues refer to the concerns raised by the way in which human beings have treated their surroundings and the long-term and possibly irreversible effects of such treatment. Most of these concerns are to do with two main interrelated areas:

- how we treat the natural world and its resources; for example, the use of fossil fuels, deforestation, acid rain and global warming
- how we treat the animal world; for example, conservation, extinction and animal cruelty.

Modern ecologists have identified four important areas that are crucial to our understanding of the environment.

- *The ecosystem.* This refers to the way in which forms of life interact with each other, such as in food chains, which link different species and interlocking elements and chemical compounds (see Figure 5.1). This interconnection must be regarded as a system where a change in the delicate balance at one point can have far reaching effects in other parts of the system. For example, introducing rabbits to Australia, where there are no natural predators, led to them overrunning the continent and possibly led to the extinction of some native animals.
- *Growth.* The environment has a limited capacity. Modern scientists have recognised that there cannot be unlimited growth. Just as the animal population in its natural environment is limited by the availability of food, territory, mates and inter species competition, so human beings must recognise that population, food consumption and pollution cannot increase indefinitely.

Figure 5.1 An ecosystem

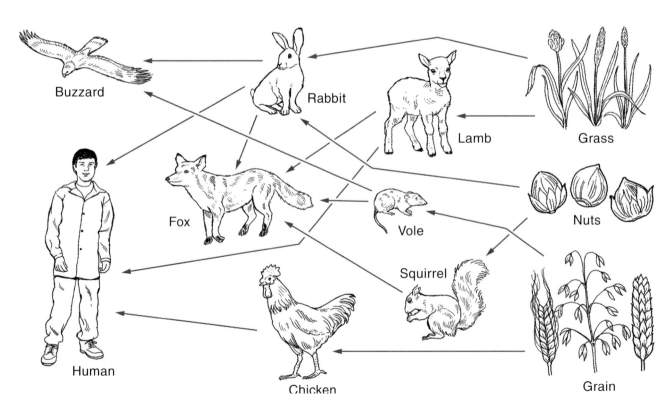

Buzzard

Rabbit

Lamb

Grass

Fox

Vole

Nuts

Squirrel

Human

Chicken

Grain

- *Ecological stability*. In the natural world, stability is maintained by a constant process of change and adjustment to continually changing conditions. Nature is never static. However, species with very small numbers of plants or animals are at much greater risk of extinction from disease, predators or changes in their food supply than species with large numbers.
- *The future*. Ecologists are concerned about the long-term effects of human intervention in nature. The natural environment needs continuity in order to flourish, so we need to consider what effect an activity carried out for short-term gain, such as chopping down trees for timber without an adequate system of replanting, may have on future generations. In relation to the age of the world as a whole, human beings have only been around for a few seconds, but the irreversible damage inflicted on the environment during that time has been immense.

Biological diversity

Diversity refers to the fact that the natural world contains at least 1.5 million different species. However, this figure only includes those that have been discovered so far. It is estimated that there may be between five and 40 million more, including 500 000 plants and untold numbers of insect species. This diversity is essential for our own survival and that of the ecosystem as a whole for the following reasons.

- The more species there are, each with its own physical characteristics, the more chance there is of resistance to natural disasters.
- Half of all our medical cures, such as morphine and quinine, come from plants. Loss of species means a loss of important natural curative substances.
- Food and natural materials used as a basis for manufacturing are based on a wide range of natural species. Extinction means a loss of important food sources.
- The complex relationships within the whole ecosystem means that the loss of one plant, for example, can mean the possible extinction of a considerable number of other animals and insects.

Attitudes to the environment

Traditionally, Christianity has based its attitudes to the environment on the Creation myths in Genesis, chapters 1–2. This suggests that the earth was created by God for a purpose and that human beings, because they are superior to animals, have a responsibility or 'stewardship' over nature. However, this attitude was later modified by the idea that it is an individual's duty to work hard and make profits. The idea that nature is there to serve human need has led to its exploitation. This was further reinforced by the ideas of mathematicians and philosophers such as Sir Isaac Newton and René Descartes. Newton's mathematical laws explaining the way in which the physical world operated, led to a *mechanistic* view of nature as consisting of impersonal masses and forces operating according to deterministic laws. Descartes argued that animals are machines without minds or feelings. Also, the Industrial Revolution encouraged the view that the natural environment was merely an inexhaustible source of raw materials. The development of capitalism also led to the view that the need for private profit justified the damage to the environment caused by industrial technology. However, Charles Darwin's work on *evolution* emphasised:

- the way in which all natural living things, including human beings, are related to each other;
- the fact that nature is not static but constantly changing to survive.

Important environmental issues

Population

The population of the world is now six billion. It is estimated that it will grow by one billion every 11 years. This population explosion has mainly taken place in underdeveloped countries and continents and it has raised the following interrelated problems for the environment.

- *Pressure on land*. As more and more people try to live off the land, it becomes exhausted. Land that is overfarmed becomes desert. Two thousand years ago, large areas of North Africa supplied the Roman Empire with wheat. Much of this once fertile land is now desert, particularly in the Sahel region of West Africa. Poverty prevents the use of more 'eco-friendly' farming methods, such as the use of fertilisers, which might help to replenish the soil.
- *Deforestation*. This problem has various causes, of which population is one. During the past 30 years, huge areas of rain forest in South America and elsewhere in the world have been chopped down. This has taken place for a variety of reasons, including the need for firewood as a fuel by poor people, for timber, for paper making, to clear the land for agriculture and to get at valuable mineral deposits. This deforestation has led to desertification through the loss of topsoil, the loss of habitat for a large number of species, resulting in their actual or near extinction, and the loss of oxygen produced by jungle vegetation, which has contributed to global warming.
- *Urbanisation*. By 2010, it is estimated that 50% of the world's population will live in towns. In poor areas, this leads to a drastic decline in local wildlife and cultivable land and a large increase in environmental damage caused by sewage, industrial waste, transport systems and other forms of pollution.

Global warming

During the past few decades there has been a noticeable increase in the world's temperature. The '*greenhouse effect*', which contributes to global warming, has been caused mainly by a vast increase in the amount of carbon dioxide released into the atmosphere through industrial processes and traffic. The effects of such warming include:

KEY words

Air pollution the release of harmful chemicals into the atmosphere by industrial processes, traffic emissions and incinerators, etc.

Biodegradable a substance that can be converted to simpler compounds by bacteria (most plastics are not biodegradable)

CFCs chlorofluorocarbons are manmade gases used in aerosols, refrigeration and air-conditioning, which are responsible for the increasing hole in the ozone layer

Composition of pure air 78% nitrogen, 21% oxygen, 1% noble gases, 0.03% carbon dioxide

Eutrophication an overgrowth of aquatic plants caused by an excess of nitrates coming into rivers from fertilisers, which causes a depletion of oxygen, killing fish

Population explosion the huge increase in the world's population, mainly occurring in developing countries

Radiation the lethal fall-out produced by the use of nuclear power and weapons, with the highest potential to do long-lasting damage

Thermal pollution releases of warm water from power stations and factories; has the same effect as eutrophication

- a rise in sea levels caused by the melting of polar ice sheets and the flooding of vast areas of low-lying land, which could ultimately displace millions of people in areas such as the Ganges delta;
- a drastic change in vegetation patterns – vast forest areas could be lost in the northern hemisphere and there would be a large increase in desert areas;
- vast animal and human migration to follow sources of food;
- possible extremes of climate and an increase in drought.

Acid rain

This important example of pollution is mainly caused by the chemicals released by smoke from fossil-fuelled power stations, such as sulphuric and nitric acid, which change rainwater from pH 5/6 to pH 3, making it more acidic. In Sweden, which receives most of Britain's acid rain, some lakes and forests have been completely destroyed by the fall-out.

Ozone layer

The ozoneosphere is a region in the upper atmosphere, between 10 and 50 km altitude, where there is much more ozone (O_3) than at lower levels. The presence of the ozone layer blocks all solar radiation of wavelengths less than 290 namometres from reaching the earth's surface. If this did not happen, most living things would die. Ozone is formed by the reaction of short-wave ultraviolet radiation from the sun on oxygen, but it is also destroyed by chlorofluorocarbons (CFC gases in aerosols) and nitrogen oxides (found in car and plane exhaust gases). The ozone layer is gradually being depleted, leading to an increase in the incidence of skin cancer in fair-skinned people. CFC gases have been banned by the developed countries, but it is expensive for developing countries to stop using them.

Animal issues

Human relate to animals in the following ways:

- as companions and working partners (e.g. guidedogs and sheepdogs);
- as zoo animals for observation, research, conservation and enjoyment;
- as food – worldwide, people eat about 140 000 000 tons of meat every year;
- for medical or product research – over 200 million animals are used annually;
- for hunting – animals are hunted for food, fashion, fun or for profit.

Recently, animal rights has become a widely discussed issue. It is no longer generally accepted that animals can be killed indiscriminately for pleasure or for profit. Poaching elephants for ivory or rhinoceroses and tigers for their horns and bones is now illegal in most countries. Causing animals pain for either medical or cosmetic purposes is now regarded by many as an infringement of basic animal rights. Many methods of animal rearing for food are now regarded as cruel (e.g. factory farming and battery hens).

Did you know?

The world's resources

- In 1990, Japan produced only 9 kg of hazardous industrial waste per head. The USA produced 1800 kg per head.

- One chlorine atom produced by CFCs can destroy 100 000 ozone atoms.

- Reserves of oil, gas and oil will be completely depleted in the next 200 years.

- Around 3 500 000 animals are killed every year in British research laboratories.

- Some rare species of tigers and rhinoceroses have less than 50 animals left.

Figure 5.2 Clean-up of the Exxon Valdez oil spill, Alaska 1989

ACTIVITIES

① Find out about the Chernobyl nuclear power station accident in 1986. Make a list of effects of the accident, then discuss the view that the advantages of nuclear power outweigh the dangers.

② What sort of immediate and/or long-term international measures would you like to introduce in order to reduce some of the damage being done by industrialised countries to the environment?

③ What reasons do you think could be used to support the use of animal experiments that involve the infliction of pain and/or death to the animals involved?

④ Should environmental considerations be more important than profit?

Conclusion

There has been a general realisation that the natural world is not a limitless, endlessly renewable resource. Human beings must learn to manage the environment so that the right of other species to life is protected and the damage caused by human pollution and activities is drastically reduced. Recent international ecological conferences have tried to draw up conservation plans, such as reducing emissions of harmful gases and the rate of deforestation. However, some countries have tended to put their short-term financial interests first. The agreements made at the 1992 UN Conference on the Environment and Development in Rio (East Summit) had still not been implemented by the end of the millennium.

Specimen exam questions

AS What are the major sources and consequences of air pollution in present-day Britain and what measures are being, or could be, taken to improve air quality?

A2 By 2050 the world's population could well have doubled to around 12 billion people. Are there just too many people in the world, or is it a question of a better and fairer distribution of the world's resources? You should consider in your response issues such as food production, energy consumption, climate, birth control, religious, social and cultural values and standard of living.

6

Genetic engineering

Genetic engineering refers to the techniques and consequences associated with the technology of altering the information carried by genes. Genes are the basic building blocks of life and they contain all the information required to enable cells to replicate themselves. The *Human Genome Project* will have mapped out the entire human genetic blue print or *genome* before 2005. One of the principal aims of genetic research is to try to correct possible and actual abnormalities present in human genes in order to improve and eradicate serious and/or life-threatening handicaps. Another important and contentious area of research is to do with the modification of plants and cereals in order to produce higher-yielding, more weather and saline-resistant and more disease-free crops. Although animal and plant stocks have been improved for several centuries through *selective breeding*, genetic engineering can operate directly upon the 'biological memory', units of information held by chemical sequences in the nucleic acid known as *DNA*.

Important areas of genetic research

Modifying plants and animals

In the early 1970s, scientists discovered that strands of DNA containing information about a particular organism could be cut using special enzymes, which could also be used to splice or cut out different genetic combinations. Genes can be *recombined* by splicing them into a bacterium, which then produces copies of that gene when it duplicates itself. Large quantities of consistently high quality and relatively cheap proteins, insulin, hormones and vaccines can be produced in this way for medical purposes.

- The gene for the protein *trypsin*, which is toxic to insects but does not harm humans, could be introduced into plant seeds.
- Wheat and other cereal crops could be modified by the introduction of bacteria from plants that have the ability to fix nitrogen from the air, thus reducing the need for expensive fertilisers.
- Other genetic modifications can increase the biodegradability of oil-based products and also help in the removal of toxic wastes and oil spills.

Risks

Many people, including scientists, have been concerned since 1973, when gene-splicing was invented, that genetically altered bacteria might escape from laboratories and multiply with unpredictable results. Strict safety guidelines have been drawn up and specially weakened strains of bacteria have been used for research in this area.

Genetically modified crops

The issue here is about the possibility that a modified gene introduced into one plant might transfer itself into another plant. For example, if a gene designed to resist herbicides, transferred to a weed, it might evolve a 'super weed' which would be resistant to any control. There are also concerns about the possible health and economic damage that may might be caused by genetic modifications. One large company has already been taken to court for trying to acquire a monopoly by selling modified seeds, which while herbicide-resistant, cannot be used to produce more than one crop. Such modified seeds are expensive and would benefit rich countries more than developing ones.

Human genetic engineering

Genetic diseases affect large numbers of people. Defective inherited genes can cause mental retardation, physical deformity or early death. Some diseases can be detected by prenatal tests, while others, such as *Huntington's disease* (which causes paralysis, mental detioration and death in middle life) can be detected in early adulthood, before the symptoms have actually appeared. This process is called *genetic screening*. Various techniques have been developed to try to alter the genetic structure that gives rise to such diseases.

Somatic-cell therapy

This technique is based on the fact that although in theory every cell in a human body carries all the information needed to grow that whole human body, it can block off the information not needed for its specialised function in a particular part of the body. This *somatic* or body cell can reproduce itself exactly and then divide. Somatic-cell change involves replacing faulty cells where the genes do not work properly with cells containing genes which do, although these new cells will themselves need renewal.

For example, with the disease of cystic fibrosis (CF), faulty CF genes, which failed to control the passage of salt and water in and out of the body's cells in the lungs, were replaced with normal ones successfully.

The next stage of research is to develop a technique that would enable self-renewing genes to be introduced so that the body will start manufacturing normal genes for itself.

Experiments have also been tried with muscular dystrophy, Tay-Sachs disease and sickle-cell anaemia, which involved the implant of white blood cells armed with a gene for a toxin that destroys tumour tissue.

Figure 6.1 Dividing cells. Left: healthy liver cells; right: cervical cancer cells.

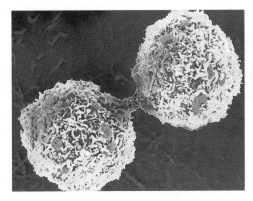
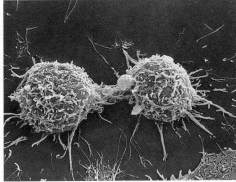

Genetics

One human cell may contain up to 100 000 genes. Most of the pioneering work in genetics was done by an Austrian monk called Gregor Mendel (1809–1884), who did thousands of experiments with pea plants to work out how characteristics were transmitted from one generation to another. In 1953, at Cambridge, Francis Crick and James Watson discovered the double helix shape and the chemical bases of DNA, for which they received the Nobel Prize.

key words

Amniocentesis prenatal screening of a foetus to look for genetic abnormalities

DNA deoxyribonucleic acid, the chemical inside molecules that contains genes

Chromosomes lengths of DNA containing genes, which can make proteins

Mutation damage to part of a genetic code which, if occurring in gametes, may result in new physical characteristics (e.g. an albino squirrel)

Somatic-cell change altering the behaviour of non-reproductive cells by the introduction of new genetic material

Germ-line therapy

Somatic-cell therapy cannot be passed on from one generation to another by sexual reproduction because the cells involved are not connected to the *gametes* or reproductive cells. In germ-line therapy, new DNA is introduced in order to *recombine* with DNA in the reproductive cells. This results in the possibility of changing the genetic profile of a child of parents who carry a genetically based disease. Once the new gene is recombined, it can be reproduced over many generations. The advantage of this type of therapy is that inaccessible brain cells or widely distributed tissue cells could be corrected in a fertilised egg . In experiments on animals, a generation of 'super mice' was developed, which grew to be 50% larger than its parents, as well as a mouse that was designed to develop cancer for use in drug tests.

Cloning

A clone can be defined as 'an individual organism that was grown from a single body cell of its parent and that is genetically identical to it' (*Encyclopaedia Britannica*).

Gene cloning can be used for all sorts of purposes. *Plasmids* (small rings of DNA) are inserted into a bacterium to produce a specified protein, so that an endless supply of copies will then be created. Such cloning is being used to produce insulin and hepatitis B vaccine, among other proteins.

Even more controversial is cloning a complete animal. The first cloned animals were frogs, when frog DNA was transplanted into a frog egg whose own genetic material had been removed. The cells began to divide to form an embryo and then a frog, which was identical to the DNA inserted into the egg.

The first successful clone of an adult animal was carried out by a team of scientists at the Roselin Institute in Edinbrugh. The nucleus of a cell from the mammary gland of an adult sheep was implanted into the embryo of another sheep's unfertilised egg, from which the nucleus had been removed. An electric current was passed through and the egg began to divide, so becoming an embryo, which was implanted into the uterus of another sheep. The lamb – Dolly – was a clone of the sheep whose mammary gland was used.

The practical implications of cloning are financially good; for example, there would be an unending supply of top-quality livestock. However, there are obviously ethical issues involved in cloning.

Important issues raised by genetic engineering

- Germ-line therapy cannot be recalled. Recombinant DNA becomes a living part of the host body and its successors.
- Like natural DNA, it becomes liable to random mutation, so that its future behaviour could be dangerously unpredictable.

- Genes tend to interact in their effects. There is no way of knowing how the introduction of one gene may affect all the others.
- If insurance companies or employers got hold of the results of someone's genetic screening they might use the information to discriminate against them in terms of insuring or employing them.
- The ability to identify the sex of or possible genetic abnormalities in a foetus means that some parents might opt for abortion in order to fulfil their expectations of a perfect child.
- In the past, *eugenic programmes* aimed at improving society have involved the selection of certain favoured human physical or mental characteristics and the deliberate destruction of those considered to be inferior. The possibility of genetic manipulation may increase this danger.
- Genetic research is very expensive and tends to be carried out by large multinational medical corporations who will 'own' the results of their research. This will give them very powerful monopolies.
- The cost of genetic treatment may result in a two-tier society, consisting of those whose parents could afford to 'improve' their offspring and those who may well be regarded as inferior.

Other ethical and religious issues

- Some critics have argued that all human genetic engineering is 'tampering with nature'; it is a violation of the principle that 'nature knows best'.
- Another religious view is that there is a permanent, universal '*natural law*', which reflects divine intentions and that genetic engineering is against what God intended.
- Other concerns have been expressed about the economic implications. Rich countries, which can afford both genetic research itself and the results of that research, will benefit the most. This will increase the gap between wealthy and poor countries.

Figure 6.2 The structure of DNA

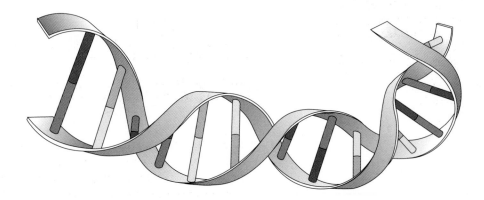

Figure 6.3   The potential of genetic modification

① 'There is something fundamentally unacceptable about any institution, corporation or individual having ownership over part of a human being' (Alistair Kent, Director of the Genetic Interest Group). What reasons could be given for this view (see Issue 14, 'The need for morality and the nature of ethical theories')?

② What evidence might be used to support the view that the advantages of genetic screening outweigh the disadvantages?

③ Read the article entitled 'Corn modified to be contraceptive' in Figure 6.3. What ethical issues do you think might be raised by such a development?

④ Is there a difference between searching for a defective gene that causes muscular dystrophy and searching for one that causes homosexuality? Split into small groups and produce arguments to defend your point of view.

Corn modified to be contraceptive

CORN has been genetically modified to make it grow a contraceptive, *writes Roger Dobson*.

In a move which could revolutionise birth control, especially in developing countries, scientists have succeeded in getting the maize to produce human antibodies to sperm.

After being harvested from the seeds of the GM corn, the antibodies are purified and processed, and then added to a lubricant designed to protect against pregnancy.

"It is an inexpensive technology and that means it can be used globally," said Dr Kevin Whaley, who has directed the research at Johns Hopkins University in America. "We envisage that it will be used topically and that it would be put into sexual lubricants. It would be something that women could apply many hours before intercourse and it would be effective for 12 to 24 hours."

Scientists envisage large acreages of the corn being grown to meet demand for what will be a relatively cheap production process. The corn, now growing in a greenhouse in San Diego, California, has been licensed for development to the biotech company Epicyte.

The technology is based on a human gene that carries the instructions for making a particular antibody or protein being transplanted into the DNA of a plant. Once in place the antibody becomes a "natural" product of that plant.

Antibodies are produced by the human immune system to counter and destroy alien bugs and viruses, but sperm is one of the few invaders that does not usually trigger an immune response in women.

However, there are some women — fewer than one in 100 — who are immune-infertile. The incoming sperm is seen by the killer cells of their immune systems as an unwanted invader and is neutralised by antibodies.

Scientists at Johns Hopkins have harnessed this antibody in the white blood cells of immune-infertile women, then cloned those cells and produced genetic material which is mixed into the DNA of the corn.

"The main concentrations are in the kernel of the corn," said Whaley. "We can keep the seeds in store and purify the protein or antibody when we need it."

Human trials should take place within two years.

The scientists are also growing a herpes antibody in corn and looking at adding others for HIV and other diseases.

Specimen exam questions

AS   Explain what is meant by genetic modification of food. Discuss the issues that arise from this practice, outlining the arguments for and against its continuing development and use.

A2   What is meant by cloning? Outline the arguments that are used to justify cloning and those that can be raised against it. Is there a difference between the cloning of animals and that of humans?

7

Transport issues

The history of transport

Boats	7000 BCE
Wheels	3500 BCE
Canals	3000 BCE
Domestication of horse	1500 BCE
Road systems	500 BCE
Canal locks	984
Iron bridges	1779
Steam ships	1807
Railways	1825
Petrol car	1885
Powered aircraft	1908

Table 7.1 *Timeline for the development of transport, 7000 BCE–1908 AD*

As transport until the nineteenth century was dependent on the horse, it is sometimes argued that the key discovery in transport was the domestication of the horse, which occurred sometime around 1500 BCE. However, others would argue that this was the discovery of boats enabling goods to be carried along rivers and across seas. The earliest boat so far discovered is a pine canoe dating from around 7000 BCE and found in Holland. Nevertheless, all modern forms of land transport rely on the invention of the wheel which was probably invented between 4000 and 3000 BCE. The wheel enabled carts, chariots and carriages to be built which allowed one horse to carry several people and considerably more goods.

All wheeled transport is restricted by the surface on which it travels. The Persians were the first to build a system of roads linking their empire in 500 BCE and were followed by the Romans whose paved roads were a masterpiece of civil engineering. It was not until the late eighteenth century that road building reached the standard set by the Romans, due to Tresaguet in France and Macadam in England. By 1830, Macadam's hardwearing small stones had been combined with bitumen to give roads a tarmac surface. Other civil engineering skills such as bridge building and tunnelling had major effects on transport. Primitive suspension and beam bridges were built in the Stone Age. The first arched bridges were built by the Romans in 250 BCE and the first iron bridge was built by Thomas Darby at Coalbrookdale, Staffordshire in 1779. The earliest underwater tunnel was built under the Euphrates in about 2000 BCE, and the first tunnel under the Thames (the Rotherhithe Tunnel) was built by Marc Brunel (Isambard Kingdom's father) between 1825 and 1843.

One way of improving transport was to build canals to join rivers. The earliest canals were built in Mesopotamia round 3000 BCE. However, canals needed a means of changing their height. This was done by locks invented by Chiao Wei-Yo in China in 984. In the eighteenth century British engineers such as Thomas Telford began a huge programme of canal building as part of the industrial revolution and developed the skills of tunnelling, embankments and cuttings necessary for the building of railways. Water transport had developed from the Egyptian single-masted wooden sailship of 3000 BCE to Chinese and European three-masted sailships of the Middle Ages. The invention of the compass, astrolabe and navigational charts allowed the European voyages of discovery in the fifteenth century (Columbus sailed to America in 1492).

The huge advance in transport came with the invention of the steam engine. The first steam engine was built by Savery in 1698, but Newcomen's 1712 engine was the first proper steam engine using a piston. However, it was not until James Watt introduced a condenser and gears that it became possible to use a steam engine for transport.

The first steam-powered ship was built by the American Robert Fulton in 1807 (the Clermont) and the first iron steamship with a screw propeller was the *SS Great Britain*, built in 1843. Several steam locomotives were designed at the beginning of the nineteenth century, but George Stephenson's *Locomotion* hauled the first public passenger railway between Stockton and Darlington in 1825. Stephenson and his son, Robert, developed the engine in *The Rocket* to use a multitubular boiler with a firebox at the rear and horizontal rather than vertical pistons. During the Railway Age (1825–1914), railways were built across all countries and continents and revolutionised not only transport, but also communications (newspapers and the telegraph)

Steam cars never became popular and the first petrol driven cars (Karl Benz, 1885) were only for the very rich. It was the mass production methods used to manufacture Henry Ford's Model T Ford (1908) that led to the next great transport revolution – the age of the car. The internal combustion engine and developments such as the pneumatic tyre (invented by Michelin), drum and disc brakes, made motor cars very attractive. The first motorways were built in Germany before the Second World War (autobahns) and from the beginning of the M1 in 1959, Britain developed an interconnected motorway system completed by the London Orbital Motorway (M25).

In a similar way, the first flying machine of the Wright Brothers (1903) had little effect on ordinary people's lives. However, after the First World War, the USA used aircraft for mail routes, and after the Second World War the development of jet airliners (Comet, 1959; Jumbo Jet (Boeing 747), 1969; Concorde, 1969) made flying faster, more comfortable and cheaper. Travel between continents, which had previously taken days or weeks on ships, now takes a matter of hours.

Science or technology?

There is often argument as to whether the advances in transport have been made by science or technology. Cayley worked out the three basic principles of flight (lift, thrust and control) in 1804, but it was another 100 years before the technology developed to make aircraft. Frank Whittle patented his theory of the jet engine in 1930, but it was 1939 before the German firm Heinkel built the first jet plane. The whole theory of electricity was discovered before Faraday invented the first electric motor (1821) but it was 1879 before an electric motor big enough to drive a vehicle was invented (Siemens' electric train).

However, the development of the steam engine seems to have been more affected by changes in technology, such as better iron and steel making and the needs of industry. Savery, Newcomen, Watt and Stephenson were all engineers with little knowledge of science. Even so, they must have developed theories, of the power of steam, for example, in order to think of a steam engine.

It appears that science and technology have always been intertwined with some scientific discoveries requiring developments in technology (e.g. particle accelerators to make discoveries in atomic physics) and some developments in technology requiring scientific theories (e.g. space travel and the earth's gravitational pull).

Transport problems

Congestion

Traffic congestion has been a problem for cities since Roman times. In the first century BCE, Julius Caesar banned wheeled traffic from Rome during daylight hours. In several European cities parking restrictions and one-way streets were introduced in the seventeenth century to deal with the congestion. The arrival of railways as a faster means of transport reduced congestion, but the age of the car has led to massive problems.

In the UK there are now more than 27.5 million vehicles on the roads. On occasions the centres of many cities experience gridlock (a traffic jam affecting a number of intersecting roads so that nothing can move). A small accident on the busiest motorways sometimes causes traffic queues of up to 25 miles. Several solutions have been proposed:

* banning cars from city centres, or charging for access to city centres (but this requires a big expansion of public transport);
* making petrol and car tax so high that people give up their cars (this also requires a big expansion of cheap public transport, otherwise people will just pay the extra to keep their cars);
* making bus lanes to give rapid transit for public transport (intersections are the major problem, where it is impossible to keep buses and cars separate);
* forcing freight onto the railways and waterways, as in much of Europe (this has the major problem of the rail and waterway systems having been run down so that there are insufficient facilities to expand);
* introducing computerisation from a traffic control centre (automatic vehicle-control system) where a vehicle is checked into a control station, gives its destination and is put into a traffic lane with its spacing to the vehicle ahead controlled by an onboard computer. (It is estimated that this could increase traffic flow from the current maximum of 2000 vehicles per hour to at least 10 000 vehicles per hour).

All of these measures (especially the expansion of public transport) will require a large government investment (which could be funded by using increased car taxes).

Pollution and energy sources

Almost all land and air transport uses fossil fuels (mainly oil), which cause pollution and are likely to run out. Car manufacturers have tackled pollution by fitting catalysers, using unleaded petrol, improving fuel consumption and recycling steel, plastic, batteries, etc. Some cars are now made of 75% recycled materials and it is estimated that it would take 50 small cars produced in 2000 to cause the same pollution as one small car produced in 1976. Car manufacturers are aiming to reduce the total tonnage of pollution caused by

KEY words

Astrolabe an instrument that can measure the height of the sun and stars to aid navigation

Dynamo a device for making electricity by using magnetism

Electric telegraph a system of sending messages over long distances by making and breaking electric connections. It was developed on the railways and by 1880 there were trans-oceanic wires allowing immediate contact between countries using Morse code

Horsepower the standard unit of power representing 550 foot per pound force per second or 746 watts

Science theories of how the universe works, e.g. how a liquid forms a gas

Technology engineering and mechanics, which may involve the application of science, e.g. a gas turbine to make electricity

Transformer a device for increasing the strength of an electric current

cars by 75% in the year 2010, compared with 1992. All these improvement will be brought about by science and technology.

The major concern is that oil supplies will run out. Consequently, railways are changing to electricity from diesel engines and car manufacturers are looking for alternative energy sources. Some firms are researching fuel-cell cars powered by the hydrogen from water, electric cars with much more efficient rechargeable batteries and even the possibility of using renewable resources such as sugar cane to produce a petrol substitute.

Safety

Death and serious injury from road accidents has gone down from 80 132 in 1985 to 44 255 in 1998, despite an increase in road traffic from 22 152 000 in 1987 to 27 538 000 in 1998.

There are many reasons for this, most of which have come from science and technology:

- the use of cameras, radar and videos has led to a greater adherence to speed limits;
- the building of more roads with carriageways separated by a crash barrier;
- the use of 'soft' signs and lamp-posts and guard rails round objects such as bridge piers;
- improved car safety features such as seat belts, collapsible steering column, air bags, side impact bars, improved brakes and tyres;
- the breathalyser to reduce 'drink' driving;
- MOT tests for older cars to keep unsafe vehicles off the road.

More improvements to safety could come from onboard computers, which could reduce speeds, warn drivers of approaching hazards, stop drivers from falling asleep, etc.

Did you know?

When's your train?

Before railways, each local community operated its own time based on the sun in its locality. The rapid transit of railways and the introduction of timetables based on the time in London led to the whole of the UK using a standard time (often known as railway time). When the railways became transcontinental, the problem became even greater and it was a Canadian railway planner, Stanford Fleming, who proposed the worldwide standard time based on 24 lines of longitude 15 degrees apart, which was adopted after a meeting of 27 countries in Washington in 1884. Each zone is 1 hour ahead or behind the next zone, based on the Greenwich meridian.

Figure 7.1 One horsepower will move 150 kg by road, 450 kg by rail and 3600 kg by canal

① Visit a local car showroom for information on safety and pollution improvements.

② Construct a file of papers on transport issues and government transport policy.

③ What scientific methods would you use to test a new fuel that is claimed to be pollution-free?

Specimen exam questions

AS   How could science and technology be used to address the transport problems of the UK?

A2   What do you think should be included in an 'integrated' transport policy for the UK? Discuss the case for *and* against a shift of emphasis from private to public transport, taking into account the needs of industry, commerce and the individual.

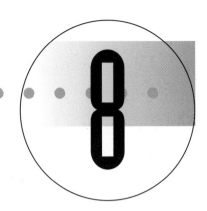

8

Energy

Energy is the capacity to do work. There are many forms of energy, e.g. *potential* (such as the string of a taut bow, which has the potential energy to fire an arrow); *kinetic* (the energy associated with movement, such as the movement of pistons in a car engine, which have the potential energy to move the car); *chemical* (the energy stored in food or fossil fuels); *gravitational* (the potential energy created when an object is raised above the earth), etc.

In physics, *the law of conservation of energy* states that energy can neither be created nor lost, it can only be transferred or converted into another form. This can be seen in creating electricity:

Figure 8.1 The creation of electricity: the law of conservation of energy

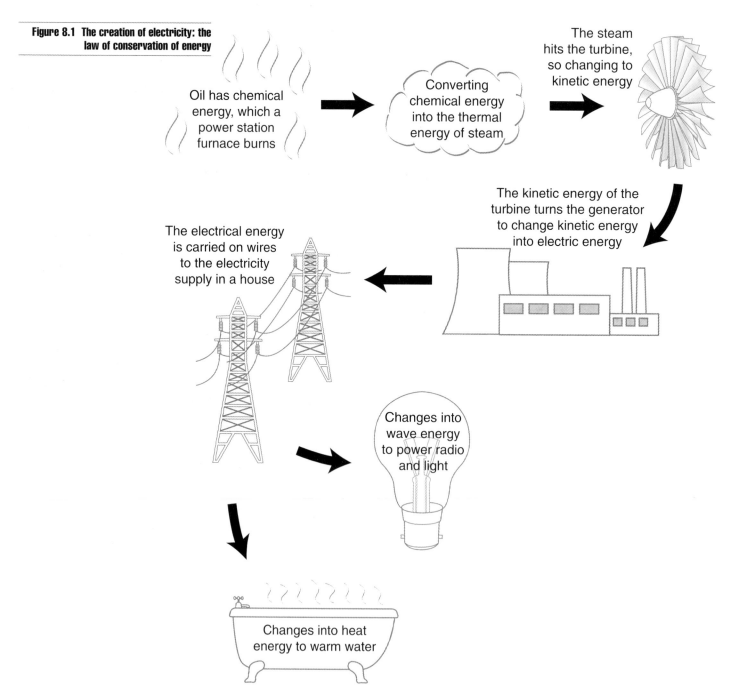

Oil has chemical energy, which a power station furnace burns

Converting chemical energy into the thermal energy of steam

The steam hits the turbine, so changing to kinetic energy

The kinetic energy of the turbine turns the generator to change kinetic energy into electric energy

The electrical energy is carried on wires to the electricity supply in a house

Changes into wave energy to power radio and light

Changes into heat energy to warm water

Another example of the conservation of energy is throwing a ball. When you throw a ball into the air, it goes up according to the energy you have put into it. All the way up its trajectory, it is gaining gravitational potential energy. When all of your energy has been converted into gravitational potential energy, the ball begins to come down.

As far as humans are concerned, the conversion of energy into usable mechanical forms has been of huge importance. All animals convert the chemical energy of food into the kinetic energy of their bodies, but humans are the only animals who have managed to convert other forms of energy for their own uses, so being able to adapt their environment, rather than having to adapt themselves to their environment (e.g. converting the heat energy of wood into the thermal energy of a fire enabled humans to live in cold climates).

Human energy conversion (the harnessing of energy)

As already stated, the first human conversion of energy was transforming wood and animal waste into fires so that the energy could be used for heating and cooking. By 5000 BCE, wood was changed into charcoal, whose greater heat was used for smelting metals. At first these were bronze (a mixture of copper and tin, both of which occur naturally); later, in about 1500 BCE, iron was produced from iron ore. This use of the energy of wood to make metals allowed humans to make tools and other implements necessary to produce other means of transforming energy. The first central heating systems were made by the Romans in about 100 BCE.

The first transfer of other energy into kinetic energy occurred in water mills, which first appeared in about 100 BCE as a means of grinding grain and olives. The Domesday Book of 1086 records a tidal mill operating at Dover (i.e. a water mill powered by the tides, rather than by a stream of water). Windmills first appeared in Iran in the seventh century. However, the great harnessing of energy did not come until the eighteenth and nineteenth centuries.

The inventions of Savery, Newcomen and Watt (see Issue 7, 'Transport issues') allowed the chemical energy of coal to change water into steam to produce the kinetic energy of a steam engine. This energy was used to drive machines (which allowed the creation of better metals, such as steel) and to revolutionise transport through the railways. In 1860, Lenoir of Belgium invented an internal combustion engine, which transformed coal into gas to move pistons. This discovery allowed Daimler to build the first petrol engine in 1883 for his motor car.

It was Faraday's discoveries in electricity, however, which led to the great changes of the twentieth century. Faraday invented an electric motor in 1821 and a transformer in 1831, from which all the inventions using electricity have been developed. So much of modern life depends on electricity that the major energy question of the twenty-first century is, 'What is the best way of transforming energy into electric energy?'.

Methods of transforming energy into electricity

Non-renewable methods

Fossil fuels such as coal and oil have chemical energy, which can be transformed into kinetic energy to drive turbines, which make electricity.

Good points	Bad points
• Very cheap to build, fairly cheap to run and very efficient.	• Fossil fuels cannot be renewed, so they will run out.
• Easy to build near to centres of population.	• Cause lots of pollution (especially acid rain and the greenhouse effect).

Nuclear fission bombards uranium with neutrons releasing *nuclear energy* to transform water into steam to drive turbines (pressurised water reactor, PWR) or using plutonium to create more atoms from the uranium and heating sodium to make steam (fast breeder reactor).

Good points	Bad points
• Fairly cheap to build, very cheap to run.	• Produce radioactive waste, needing special storage for thousands of years.
• No pollution.	• Danger of leaks with huge health risks (e.g. Chernobyl).
• Very efficient.	• Fuels can be used for nuclear weapons.
	• Reactors must be built near large water supplies for cooling, usually on the coast.
	• Uranium and plutonium resources will eventually run out.

Natural gas (a fossil fuel produced in the same way as oil and gas) is now being used to fuel power stations.

Good points	Bad points
• Cheap to build and run.	• A fossil fuel, so it will eventually run out.
• Very efficient.	• Transport can cause problems, as the gas is highly explosive.
• Easy to build near centres of population.	
• Much less pollution than other fossil fuels.	

Semi-renewable methods

Geo-thermal energy (the heat from the rocks in the earth's core) can be used to create steam to drive turbines. The first geothermal power stations used the steam from hot water springs and were not very efficient, but over the past 20

SCIENCE, MATHEMATICS AND TECHNOLOGY

years new methods of drilling have allowed two deep holes to be sunk to near the earth's mantle; water is sent down one hole and it comes back up the other as steam to drive a turbine.

Good points	Bad points
• Fairly cheap to build. • Very cheap to run. • No pollution. • It will take a long time for the heat source to disappear.	• Only creates small amounts of electricity. • Production depends on special geological features, so there is a restricted number of places where they can be built.

Energy from waste is a recent innovation in the UK, where incinerators are changed into power stations to transform the energy of the waste into electricity, instead of just burning it. Some countries are experimenting with sewage power stations, which would be completely renewable and possibly more efficient.

Good points	Bad points
• Cheap to build. • Very cheap to run. • Efficient. • A good way of getting rid of waste.	• They cause pollution (but not as much as oil and coal), but the pollution would be caused anyway in getting rid of the rubbish. • The more recycling there is, the less fuel there will be.

Renewable methods

The most efficient renewable method is *hydroelectric power* (HEP), which converts the energy of flowing water into mechanical energy to drive turbines.

Good points	Bad points
• Very cheap to run. • Very efficient. • Causes no pollution. • Fuel will never run out.	• Very expensive to build. • Can only be built in certain areas, well away from cities. • Long lines of pylons are required to transport the energy to civilisation. • Huge areas of land have to be swamped in order to fuel the plant.

Wind generators are now widely used to transform wave energy of wind into electricity.

Hawaii now has a wind station producing 1500 megawatts, equivalent to a fossil fuel power station.

Good points	Bad points
• Fairly cheap to build. • Very cheap to run. • Cause no pollution. • Energy source will never run out.	• Not very efficient; each set of blades only produces a small amount of electricity. • Have to be built in wide open spaces and are a very prominent feature in the landscape.

Horse power?

The main source of energy in the world is still wood. In most developing countries people have to use firewood for heating and cooking. This is a major cause of deforestation and soil erosion. An alternative source of energy, in the form of dung, can be provided by humans and animals. This is converted into gas in a biogas plant (see Figure 8.2), which is easy to build and maintain.

Solar energy can be directly transformed into electricity using silicon or gallium arsenide cells. Other methods involve storing the heat and using it not only to produce electricity, but also to power heating systems, etc.

Good points	Bad points
• Very cheap to run.	• Expensive to build.
• Cause no pollution.	• Need to cover a large area to produce a reasonable amount of power.
• Energy source will never run out.	• More suitable for hot, sunny countries.

The *energy of the sea* can be converted into electricity through either tide or wave power stations. The Rance river estuary in France has a *tidal power station*, which drives turbines by damming the tide. In Japan there is an oscillating water column, which converts the *energy of the waves* to create an air turbine that drives a generator.

Good points	Bad points
• Very cheap to run.	• Very, very expensive to build.
• Cause no pollution.	• Not very efficient yet.
• Energy source will never run out.	• Can only be built in certain areas.

Figure 8.2 A biogas plant

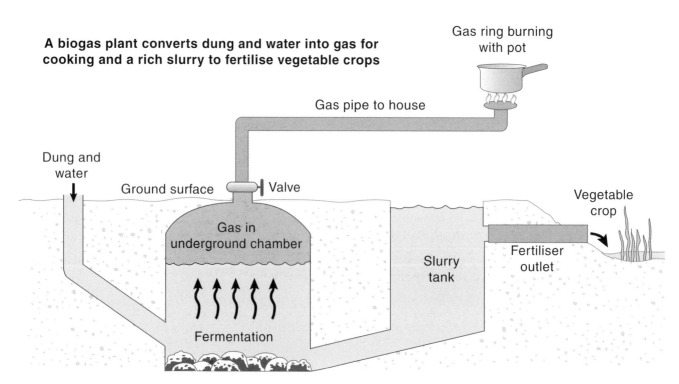

A biogas plant converts dung and water into gas for cooking and a rich slurry to fertilise vegetable crops

① Investigate how much of your daily life is dependent on electricity.

② Think of an example other than the power station to illustrate the law of conservation of energy.

③ If you could begin electricity generation from scratch, which methods of generating electricity would you choose, and why?

④ Explain, with illustrations, why energy can only be converted, not created.

Specimen exam questions

AS   What are the major sources of renewable energy in the UK? What are the current limitations in terms of their development and use?

A2   'Research into alternative energy resources to replace oil should be funded by government, not by private industry.' To what extent do you agree with this view? You should refer to economic, political and ethical values, as well as to the nature of scientific research in your answer.

9

Computers

A computer is an electronic machine, which can store and perform calculations and process data at very high speeds. Computers require programmes (sequence of operations) by which the computer can process the data to produce the intended outcome. For example, if a manufacturer wants a business to be able to input all its billing data so that the computer can output individual bills, the programmer has to work out every step of the process and write each step into a command performable by the computer. Since their invention, computers have revolutionised many aspects of life and now affect everyone.

The history of computers

It is generally accepted that Charles Babbage designed the prototype computer in 1834. It was a machine that could both perform and store the results of calculations. However, it was too complicated to build. In 1945, Eckert and Maunchly built the Electronic Numerical Integrator and Calculator in America, but this was more like a giant calculator than a computer, as it could not store information.

It was the invention of the *transistor* (a miniature device to amplify electronic signals) and the *printed electronic circuit* (replacing the copper wires used for carrying the electric current with a small board) that allowed the building of the first computer, the Manchester Mark I. The first computer to be sold commercially was the Ferranti Mark I in 1951. In 1958 Texas Instruments produced integrated circuits on a silicon chip. The major breakthrough in computing came in 1969 when Hoff of the USA developed the *microprocessor* by placing all the circuits that do the work of a computer onto a single silicon chip. The era from 1970 to 1999 is often referred to as the Microprocessor Revolution, similar in impact to the Industrial Revolution of 1750–1850.

Early computers were huge, but the invention of the microprocessor allowed the developed of much smaller computers and the first personal computers (PCs) that could be used in homes. The first PC was the Altair, marketed in 1975, which never achieved great success because it came in kit form and had to be assembled at home. The first successful PC was the Apple II, which was small enough and cheap enough to be used in small businesses, schools, offices and homes. In 1981, IBM introduced their PC, which was no faster than the Apple, but used the Microsoft Corporation's operating system MS-DOS, which became the industry standard so that any competitors had to market their equipment as '*IBM compatible*'.

During the 1980s and 1990s, operating systems and microprocessors developed to give greater speed and memory, but the next big development was the CD-ROM, which allowed computers to use digital sound and video images, so becoming 'multimedia'. However, the most important computer development of the 1990s was the *World Wide Web* (WWW) and the connected *Internet*. The Web was released to the public in 1992 and by 1999 there were millions of users worldwide.

Types of computer

Although most people are likely only to use PCs, there are many different types of computer. The largest are called *supercomputers* and are mainly used in scientific research, such as the particle laboratory in Geneva and are designed for shared use. Next are the *mainframe computers*, which are also designed for several users and are often used as a central repository for a mass of data, which is accessed through a network by PCs or workstations. Next is the *minicomputer*, which can be used to power a small network, or can be used by scientific researchers; again, it is for multiple use. Slightly less powerful than the minicomputer is the *workstation*, which is used in scientific research, engineering and business. A workstation, like a PC, is designed for the exclusive use of a single person.

Personal computers come in four types. The largest PCs are not portable and are known as *desktop computers*. Large portable PCs, which fit on your knee, are called *laptops*, whereas book-size ones are called *notebook computers*. The smallest pocket-sized computers are called *palm-sized computers*.

Computer networks are collections of computers (or terminals equipped with microprocessors such as supermarket tills) interconnected by telephone lines or other high speed communication links to exchange data or process information. The network can be a national one (such as those connecting shops with credit card centres), a local one (known as a LAN – local area network) restricted to an area or an organisation or even to a building. Networks connected by telephone lines require a *modem* (modulator/demodulator) to convert the digital impulses from the computer into the analog impulses required for telephone lines. Networks require coaxial or fibre-optic cables for fast data transmission and easy installation.

Uses of computers

Computers began as an aid to scientific research and to the defence industry. However, they are now used in every area of business and life. In industry, computers are used for flexible manufacturing systems (FMS) and computer-integrated manufacturing (CIM).

CIM begins with the design of a new product, which can be done much more efficiently by CAD (computer-aided design). The designer creates a drawing of the product (as a draughtsman would), then stores the drawing and uses various pieces of software to test the effects of heat, pressure, etc. on the new product. The results of these tests can then be incorporated into the design and detailed drawings drawn by the computer, so that the production team can make a prototype, which has already undergone many tests and adjustments without the time and expense of making products.

After the design, computers are used to formulate the best method of manufacture (computer-aided manufacturing, CAM). If there is a continuous manufacturing process, computers can be used to control the whole process. A

KEY words

Algorithm a set of rules used for calculation or problem solving

Analog using signals or information represented by a continuously variable quantity, such as spatial position or voltage (the English form is analogue)

Bit a unit of information expressed as a choice between two possibilities (also called binary notation)

Byte a group of eight bits operated as a unit

Clients programmes that request documents from a server as users ask for them

Database a structured set of information held in a computer, which can be accessed in different ways, e.g. a list of customers and suppliers

Desk-top publishing using a desk-top PC's word-processing, images, charts, tables, etc. together

Digital using signals or information represented by digits (regarded as more efficient than analogue)

Floppy disc a disc that can be put into a computer to store information outside the computer

Hard copy a printout on paper

Hard disc the part of the computer that stores information in the computer

Hardware computers

Megabyte a million characters

Memory how much data can be stored by a computer

Server computer programs that store and transmit data to other computers on the network

Software programs and systems that are put into a computer

computer will measure the important process variables such as temperature, flow rate and pressure. Then it works out the best manufacturing strategy and operates the devices (switches, valves, furnaces, etc.) in the manufacturing process to achieve the strategy. Finally, the computer produces management reports on production performance, product quality, etc. If there is no continuous process, the computer will plan the processes required for the most efficient production of the product.

The computer will then be involved in the business system: ordering raw materials and organising stock control, customer orders, employee payroll, customer service, etc. All this use of the computer is aimed at achieving the optimum product and profit for the company.

FMS is based on machine tools being linked together by a *material handling system* controlled by a computer. The computer system works out which machine should be doing what and organises the materials for them. This should result in the system being able to operate at maximum performance whether a machine breaks down, there is a shortfall of supplies or whatever, but it requires the firm to invest in machine tools that can be computer controlled.

Business and commerce are now using computers in many ways. All the data used for customer accounts, personnel, etc. is computerised to increase speed and efficiency. Shops find that computerisation can have major benefits. When Boots installed *point-of-sale terminals* to a central computer, all stock control and ordering was taken away from local stores. This enabled the company to see which lines were not profitable, it ended stock checking and reduced the need for warehousing. As a result of the computerisation, Boots increased their profits by £50–60 million a year. Banks are able to use their own networks to reduce the need for cash being moved around the country. The bank computerisation that affects most workers in the country is the BACS system, which enables firms to pay wages into individual workers' accounts without cash being used.

Networking has also made it possible for businesses to encourage their employees to work from home using a PC connected to a network. This saves the company a considerable amount of money in providing the office space for that worker.

The Internet

The Internet is a network connecting many computer networks based on a system called *transmission control protocol/Internet protocol*. It was established in 1983 to enable academics at universities around the world to share research with each other. The original uses of the Internet were electronic mail (e-mail letters sent immediately to another computer anywhere in the world) and newsboards or bulletin boards giving information. However, the development of the World Wide Web in 1989 by Tim Berners-Lee and colleagues at CERN, a European scientific laboratory researching the nature of matter in Geneva, transformed the Internet.

The Web converts documents into hypertext and then stores them so that

Did you know?

Chips with everything

The silicon chip (see Figure 9.1) is produced by growing silicon (a type of quartz) artificially and cutting it into thin slices. The circuit information to be put onto the chip is then drawn out 250 times larger than it will be on the chip. The circuit design is then reduced to chip size and photographically copied 500 times onto the slice. The slices are placed in an oven and heated with different chemicals. The atoms of the chemicals attach themselves to the silicon along the lines of the circuits, which are then joined by fine wires. The slice is then cut into 500 chips (all containing the same information) by a laser saw.

Figure 9.1 The silicon chip

they can be accessed through a word in the text. It also allows hypermedia documents (documents featuring images, sounds and moving pictures) to be accessed. The Web was made available to the public as part of the Internet in January 1992, and since then many companies have set up *Internet providers* (*search engines*) to allow individuals and businesses to use the Internet and the World Wide Web. The main ones are AOL (America On Line) and Microsoft Network. Obviously, the fees for using the Internet are mainly determined by the company owning the connecting cables. In the UK this is mainly BT, though some cable telephone/television companies are installing Internet cables, e.g. NTL.

So many Internet businesses have been established that in 1999 it was possible for a man isolated in a room with access only to the Internet, to be able to obtain all the food, drink, clothes, furniture, etc. he needed simply by clicking his mouse button. Most firms now have a web site to advertise their business or to enable orders to be made by e-mail. Many Internet companies have been established to provide special Internet services. For example, it emerged in January 2000 that there is an Internet company that will provide addresses of people who have ex-directory telephone numbers (some unknown person used this service to discover Jill Dando's address). The Internet also allows small companies to advertise worldwide for a very small cost; some such companies, such as specialist cheese manufacturers, are finding their sales rocketing.

Another possibility of the Internet is *interactive media*, meaning that television, music and radio can be accessed by an individual at a PC. Already MP3 enables Internet users to download music from the Internet onto special Walkmans. This could revolutionise the media industry and is thought to be the reason behind the merger between AOL and Time Warner, in January 2000, which created the world's largest company. AOL's Internet connections can now use all the films, cartoons, television programmes, music and magazine articles of Warner Brothers. It also has access to television stations to advertise itself, and probably to use new technology to allow Internet access through cable and digital television.

The Internet's major revolution has been *freedom of information*. It is impossible to censor the Internet as there is so much going on that no one would know where to start. Even in 1995, when the number of Internet subscribers was only about 25 million, the volume of information exchanged on 'the Net' was enough to fill 30 million books of 700 pages each!

The future

The phenomenal changes during the 1990s mean that no one can tell what will happen in the future.

Some, such as the science fiction novelist William Gibson who invented the term, believe that *cyberspace* will arrive. This means an artificial environment created by computers. People will work and be entertained via their PC.

Others believe that work patterns will be changed by networking and that the Internet will take over a lot of shopping. However, people will still be

required to process orders made via the Internet, to deliver goods ordered by the Internet, to produce the goods ordered by the Internet, to make the music and television programmes downloaded from the Internet, and so on. There is already some evidence that people do not want to work at home. Part of the value of work is the social element, meeting different people, forming friendships, gossiping, etc. and people do not want to give these up. Also many people find it difficult to work at home – there are distractions such as the family, and temptations, such as daytime television!

Others believe that there are signs that the Internet is peaking. Internet only traders, such as Amazon, had poor Christmas trading figures in 1999. There are signs that retailers such as Wal-Mart who are offering on-line shopping in addition to their superstores (Wal-Mart is American, but owns Asda) will take the Internet market as they can offer better prices. There are also indications that people see the Internet as little different from catalogue shopping and would rather go to the shops. Some families have been put off the Internet by cases such as that of Gary Glitter, which show how many paedophiles are on the Internet. The very freedom of information on the Net means that parents can only exercise control by being in the room all the time that their children are on line. The Jill Dando murder is only one of many signs of Internet stalking. This may lead parents to decide that the safest way is to have no Internet connection. Some people are worried that they have to give credit card or bank details to shop on the Internet and that these details can then be hacked into.

There is no doubt, however, that computers will continue to play an ever greater part in industry and business, and so in everyone's lives. The information available on the Internet is also so great that it will become essential for schools and colleges to have access.

Specimen exam questions

AS 'The computer has caused more problems for society than benefits.' Discuss to what extent you believe this statement to be true.

A2 'Our lives are now dominated by computers and electronic communications to the extent that they control us, rather than we control them. Furthermore, this domination is likely to increase, rather than decrease.' What is you opinion of this view and what, if anything, do you think we should do about the role of these technologies in our lives?

ACTIVITIES

① Ask a computing teacher how companies make money from the Internet.

② Look in the business pages of a quality newspaper to see what is happening to computer companies.

③ Make a list of how your life is affected by computers, and what effects you think computers will have on your life over the next 10 years.

10

Medical developments

The application of scientific method and technology to the problems of the human body has led to enormous advances in the capacity of medicine to deal with life-threatening diseases, both in terms of prevention and cure. Many once fatal or dangerous conditions can now be treated successfully. Diseases such as smallpox have been eradicated in most of the world. Tuberculosis and diphtheria, for example, no longer kill enormous numbers of people, particularly children, in many developed countries. National health systems, which utilise *vaccination programmes*, have led to continuing improvements in public health so that diseases such as rickets, measles, poliomyletis and whooping cough no longer represent the same threat to the quality of life or to life itself. Other important medical advances, often interrelated, have been made in such areas as:

- genetics
- embryo and reproductive technology
- immunology
- neurology and scanning techniques
- surgery and transplants.

Genetics (see Issue 6, 'Genetic engineering')

Arguably, genetic research has been the most spectacular and far-reaching area of medical development in the twentieth century. Genetic screening, which examines human beings for malfunctioning or defective genes, will soon be as commonplace as blood tests and it will be linked to procedures that can replace or repair genetic damage. The results of the *Human Genome Project*, which has been set up to map all the genes in the human body, will not only identify differences in genetic make-up in different ethnic populations, but also help to identify possible causes of various diseases and conditions. *Germline gene therapy* will enable genetic changes to be made to those cells that transmit information from one generation to another, thus enabling permanent changes to be made. Diseases already identified as having genetic components include asthma, leukaemia, sickle-cell anaemia, Huntington's disease, diabetes and cancer.

Developments in genetic technology have also led to the possibility of *cloning*. This involves the exact duplication of one human being's genetic code in order to reproduce an identical person. In 1998, the Human Genetics Advisory Committee argued that cloning in order to produce 'spare parts' such as kidneys or livers should be allowed but that the cloning of complete human beings should be banned. One of the advantages of cloning human tissues is that they would not be rejected by the human being from whom they were originally cloned.

Embryo and reproductive technology

Medical advances in this area now mean that infertility no longer automatically leads to childlessness. There are now thirteen different ways to have a baby other than through sexual intercourse, including:

- *In vitro fertilisation*. This was first developed in the 1960s by the British gynaecologist Patrick Steptoe and involves the removal of an egg from a woman's womb, which is then fertilised by the husband's sperm in a test tube or culture dish. The process has partly depended on the ability to remove embryos successfully from the womb, to store them at freezing temperatures and to re-implant them.
- *Surrogacy*. Infertile couples now have the possibility of genetically related children through surrogacy. This involves the implantation of an embryo into the womb of a woman who is not genetically related but who will carry the embryo until the child is born and then return it to the real parents. Embryos can also be created in the test tube for research purposes but may only be used for up to 14 days after fertilisation.
- *Fertility drugs*. These have been developed as an aid to overcoming infertility and to increase the chance of a woman conceiving. They often involve '*superovulation*', which results in the production of more ripe eggs than would normally be produced. This can lead to the problem of multiple births, which may damage rather than enhance the possibility of survival of embryos.

Immunology

Immunology is 'the study of resistance to disease in humans and animals'. Great developments have taken place in this field in the second half of the twentieth century, particularly since the discovery that the body's immune system is based on the activities of various types of white blood cells, found in blood, lymph vessels and tissue fluids. The main centres of activity are the *thymus*, *spleen* and *lymph nodes*. An immune response is triggered when the body detects the presence of a foreign body. By 1900, medical technology had already identified serum defence and developed vaccinations and antitoxins against such killer diseases as cholera, rabies, bubonic plague and typhoid. Important work on blood cells was done by *Karl Landsteiner* (1868–1943), whose experiments led to the possibility of blood transfusions. Further immunological research has led to a greater understanding of why transplanted organs are rejected by the host body and this has saved thousands of lives. In the 1970s, *molecular biology*, *cell biology* and *immunochemistry* have shared spectacular interconnected results, in particular, a greater understanding of the way cancers and human immuno-deficiency (HIV) develop, although there are as yet, no certain cures.

Did you know?

Trust me: I'm a doctor

- 1.3 million new cases of cancer occur in the USA every year.
- The first nephrectomy (surgical removal of a kidney) took place in 1861.
- The first X-rays were produced by Karl Wilhelm Roentgen in 1896.
- The first pacemaker was inserted into a heart in 1959.
- In 1930 a woman had a one in thirty chance of dying during or because of child birth. In 1990 the chance was less than one in 250 000.
- In 1997, a 63-year-old woman gave birth after a successful *in vitro* fertilisation.

Neurology and scanning techniques

Following on the work of several seminal researchers in the late nineteenth century, particularly in relation to the minute electrical charges produced by certain functions of the brain, scanning techniques have been developed that have helped us to understand how the brain works. Specific 'brain waves', produced by impulses emanating from the cerebral cortex and reflecting states of consciousness, external stimuli and 'mental' operations, can be used to diagnose malfunctions such as epilepsy. Further work on these brain waves has helped with the diagnosis of psychiatric disorders, migraine and blood pressure, as well as contributing to sleep research. Recent developments in scanning technology have helped scientists to build up a far more accurate picture of the central nervous system and the damage done to it by strokes or Alzheimer's disease. Neuroscientists such as the Nobel prize-winning *Gerald Edelman* have developed sophisticated maps to show how flexible and adaptable the brain actually is. To a certain extent, some parts of the brain can take over functions damaged elsewhere. This research has also led to a greatly increased ability to diagnose and cure a wide range of psychiatric and personality problems.

Surgery and transplants

Acquired immuno-deficiency syndrome (AIDS) a usually fatal breakdown in the body's immune system caused by a virus which destroys white blood cells

Angioplasty a surgical technique that clears a blocked artery by inserting a tiny balloon in order to clear away obstructions

Antibodies protein molecules produced to combat microbial infection and provide immunity

Electrocardiograph a machine that records the minute electrical currents produced by the heart

Immunisation the artificial creation of immunity to disease by vaccination

Advances in surgery have been driven partly by the need to treat dreadful wounds received during wartime. Up until the Second World War, many surgeons believed that a wide range of medical conditions could be cured by the 'knife', including tumours, tuberculosis, throat cancer, hernias, etc. However, it took a long time before many of these operations developed a high success rate, based on improved sterilisation and increased understanding of how internal organs and cell growth actually work. Enormous strides have been made in heart surgery. In 1931, Werner Fossman, injected a radio-opaque substance via a catheter into his heart, thereby allowing the first heart X-ray to take place. This was followed by the technique of forcing a tiny balloon through a constricted artery in order to clear it and allowing the heart to function properly. By 1939, surgeons were able to suture and repair damage to the walls of the heart without a strong risk of infection. The development of the heart–lung machine, which takes over the functions of these organs, has led to the replacement of blocked arteries leading to the heart and the use of artificial valves and pacemakers.

Transplants

In modern times, the emphasis in surgery has changed from *excision* – cutting and removal – to *replacement* and *plastic surgery*. This can include:

- removal of skin tumours, cleft palates and cleft lips
- skin grafts to repair burn damage and scars – these techniques were significantly improved by *Archibald McIndoe*, who developed reconstructive and plastic surgery in response to the horrific burns suffered by young Air Force pilots in the Second World War.

Organ transplants involving the replacement of lungs, liver or spleen and particularly kidneys have drastically increased their success rate because of:

- a greater understanding of how immune reactions work
- the recognition that the tissue types of the organ being transplanted had to be matched exactly with those of the recipient
- the development of immunosuppressive drugs such as cortisone and cyclosporine.

Many of these recent developments in medicine have saved thousands of lives and made the lives of the chronically ill or disabled far more bearable. However, the technology involved is hugely expensive. National Health Service hospitals with limited resources have to make 'life and death' decisions such as who should have access to a kidney dialysis machine, or whether such scarce resources be 'wasted' on the old. The desperate shortage of organs such as hearts and livers means that difficult decisions have to be made about who should have them. Progress in medicine brings with it complex ethical issues.

Figure 10.1   AIDS viruses on the surface of a T-lymphocyte cell

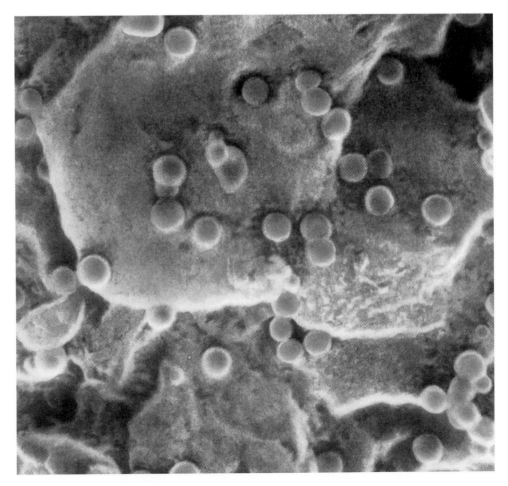

① Advances in genetics may soon allow the possibility of designing babies in advance so that they reflect the intellectual and physical characteristics desired by the parents. What dangers do you think might follow from this practice?

② What criteria would you use to decide which patients should be allowed the use of a kidney dialysis machine and why?

③ Which branch of the National Health Service should have the most money spent on it and why?

Specimen exam questions

AS Scientific research often involves difficult ethical issues. Discuss the scientific principles and ethical issues involved in any of the following: the use of animals in research; IVF and other forms of assisted human reproduction; genetic testing in humans; alteration of germ cell DNA.

A2 'Society should be grateful that science, through genetically modified foods, has provided the means to solve the world's food shortage.' Critically evaluate this statement from the perspectives of science, society and morality.

The impact of science on culture

Ampère a French scientist who discovered the connection between electricity and magnetism

Babbage English mathematician who invented the first, very basic, computer

John Logie Baird Scottish inventor of television

Alexander Bell Scottish–American inventor of the telephone

Karl Benz German inventor of the first petrol-driven car

Biro Hungarian inventor of the ballpoint pen

Crick and Watson English and American scientists who discovered the double helix structure of DNA

Daguerre French inventor of photography

Charles Edison American inventor of the record player and the light bulb

Hertz German scientist who discovered radio waves

Guttenberg German inventor of the printing press

Leeuwenhoek Dutch inventor of the microscope

Linnaeus Swedish scientist who developed the system for classifying plants

Lippershey Dutch inventor of the telescope

Lumière brothers French inventors of the motion-picture camera (cinematographe)

Marconi Italian inventor of the radio

Nobel Swedish scientist who discovered dynamite and established Nobel prizes

Louis Pasteur French scientist who established that germs are the cause of disease and introduced pasteurisation to prevent germs in milk

Rutherford New Zealand scientist who was the first to split the atom

Whittle English engineer who invented the jet engine

Wright brothers American designers of the first powered aircraft

One of the most important impacts of technology on culture has been printing. Printing enabled the rise of literature (especially novels) and such developments as newspapers. It can be argued that printing has been the major development of the second millennium, as it allowed ideas and information to spread rapidly. When books had to be written by hand, it was easy to prevent information from spreading, but it was almost impossible after the invention of the printing press. The Reformation could not have happened without printing, and it is possible that the scientific revolution would not have occurred either.

Science has had some major effects on music, not only in such things as the invention of the piano (around the middle of the eighteenth century), but also such things as amplifiers, electronic instruments, synthesisers, etc. Perhaps the major effect was the invention of the gramophone. This was the musical equivalent of printing. Prior to the record, people could only hear live performances where audiences would be measured in thousands at most; after the record, audiences were measured in millions. Of course, the music industry has also been affected by the invention of radio, television and video – what effect has the invention of video had on the promotion of popular music?

Theatre, opera and the ballet have all been affected by scientific advances in construction, lighting and design, which enable a much wider range of staging and special effects (the special effects that science has given to the cinema, e.g. *Star Wars* and the Bond films have been adapted for use in theatres). It was thought that the scientific inventions of film and television would kill off live theatre, but this has not been the case. In fact, just as television has improved and popularised film (investigate how many great British films have been produced by Channel 4 television), so both television and film encourage people to go to the theatre. (How many TV soap stars appear in Christmas pantos at the theatre?) All theatres and live music shows now use computers, especially to control the lighting and other special effects.

Art has always been affected by science. It was the discovery of oil paints that led to the great revolution in painting in the fifteenth century. The invention of photography led to changes in painting in the nineteenth century as people became less interested in portrait painting so that Impressionism could develop. Sculpture has been affected by new tools and, particularly over the past 50 years, by welding and discoveries in metallurgy. Computers enable designs and graphics to be developed by artists in different ways. Artists have now much more chance of a commercial career through such things as cartoon films and computer games.

The impact of science on religion is dealt with in Issue 2 ('Religion and science') and should be included in any essay on the impact of science on culture.

The impact of science on society

Science has had tremendous effects on society. Issues 7, 8 and 9 ('Transport issues', 'Energy' and 'Computers') could be used for any examination questions. The changes made to society by the inventions of railways, steam ships, cars and planes are not confined to having holidays abroad. Newspapers, the growth of suburbs where workers can live away from their factories, the possibility of all types of goods being transported round the world (until the growth of air freight, such fruits as strawberries could only be eaten in June and July) are all the product of scientific advances. The inventions of electricity, telephones, radio, television, film, records have revolutionised the ways in which humans can communicate. They have also revolutionised society. Entertainments that would have only been available to the very rich are now available in everyone's living room.

When combined with the effects of computers and the development of the Internet and e-mail, science has changed society from small communities in small nation states into what is now called 'the global village'. This term means many things:

- that what happens in one area of the world is immediately known elsewhere in the world;
- that finance and commerce are so worldwide that everyone is interdependent (see Issue 31, 'Economic theories');
- that the same things can be bought anywhere in the world (e.g. McDonalds);
- that there is a similar culture and set of values throughout the world.

There are those who argue that there is no such thing as a global village as there are so many differences between societies. However, one of the best indicators of how science has led to the world becoming a global village was the way in which the millennium was celebrated around the world, especially in countries such as Japan and Pakistan, where the indigenous culture has a different dating system. The effects of the scientific revolutions in transport and communications have been that all societies are now using the western dating systems, as such things as the Internet require common dating and time zones. For this reason the AD and BC letters (identifying the system as Christian) are being replaced by CE (Common Era) and BCE (Before the Common Era), so that the system can be used by anyone whatever their religion or culture.

Perhaps the greatest effect that science has had on society has been the way in which science has replaced religion or the government as the basic authority behind society. The fact that science is now the source of authority has also required the advance of democracy. Science requires that everyone has to have equality of opportunity, as ability and truth are the only criteria for someone's ideas to be accepted. Science can only thrive in a free society where thinkers can exchange ideas.

Some historians claim that science was the cause of the fall of the Soviet Union in the Cold War. The communist countries and NATO countries never actually fought each other, but kept developing more and more advanced weapons so that there was mutually assured destruction, resulting in the Star Wars programme (weapons in space which could block an opponent's missiles). This bankrupted the Soviet Union, leading to the collapse of communism.

Rotten science?

Many artists see aesthetic value in the discoveries of science. A sculptor, Rachel Chapman, and a microbiologist, Dr Jane Nicklin, worked together in 1999 to create a living work of art. 1040 agar-filled petri dishes were filled with mould cultures commonly found growing on domestic foodstuffs and arranged to create a palette of textures and colours. The moulds were grown in the biology labs of Birkbeck College, London University and timed to be incorporated into the sculpture so that the colours were in artistic order, yet constantly changing. They called their work of art, Sapros (from *sapro*, meaning 'putrefying').

The exhibition was very successful. Of the relationship between science and the arts, Rachel Chapman said, 'A lot of the things you do as an artist are science-based, but most artists have no understanding of it at all. Physics and chemistry come into play when we manipulate the composition of paints or the reactions of materials under different stimuli.' Dr Jane Nicklin said, 'The more I understand art, the more comfortable I feel with some of the other things I do. In both ecology and physics, balance and the beauty of an idea are important concepts.' (*Birkbeck College Magazine*, June 1999).

The impact of culture and society on science

In the same way that science has had great effects on culture and society, so society and culture have had effects on science.

There are thinkers who argue that without the Reformation, modern science would not have been able to develop. Galileo was silenced by the Inquisition, but in countries such as England, Holland, Scotland and the Protestant German states his ideas were able to flourish. Indeed, Descartes moved to Holland so that he could have the freedom to publish his ideas. There is also a great connection between the rise of capitalism and the rise of science. Capitalism led to industrialisation and the two together encouraged scientists as new inventions were going to lead to greater profits for the capitalists. Capitalism also requires freedom (scholars such as Weber and Tawney have argued for a connection between Protestantism and the rise of capitalism) and so capitalist societies had the necessary freedom of thought for the rise of science. Science has often been funded by capitalism, either through research carried out in

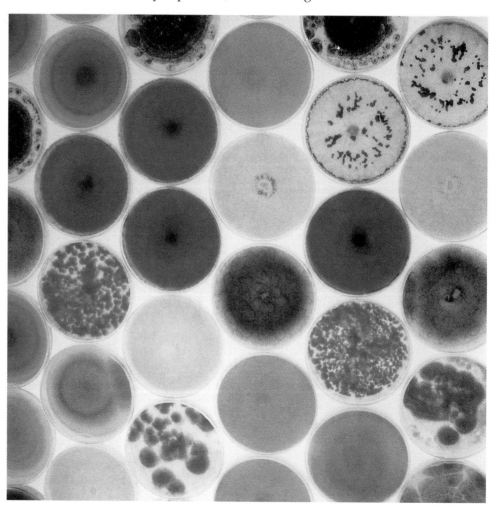

Figure 11.1 Sapros (Source: Birkbeck College Magazine, June 1999)

ACTIVITIES

① Choose an area of culture in which you are interested (e.g. pop music) and investigate how far it has been affected by science and technology.

② Investigate your own life (home, school, entertainment) to see what effects science and technology have on you.

③ Choose an area of design (e.g. a new car) and assess how far culture has had an effect on the science and technology involved.

④ Evaluate the scientific, economic, political and moral arguments that could be used to argue for and against a greater privatisation of the National Health Service.

industry or through university research funded by capitalism. You need to ask such questions as whether some scientific advances, such as genetically modified crops or cloning, would have been developed if capitalism was not offering great profits to the scientists.

Perhaps the other great effect of culture and society on science is that some scientific advances have been halted or altered because society's values are opposed to the changes. For example, the generally accepted ethic is that life is sacred (even atheists accept that human life should be treated as a gift, even though not a gift from God); consequently, scientific attempts to clone humans or to develop brain transplants have been stopped by society's culture. Clearly, there has always been a tension between society's culture and values and the free advance of science. Synoptic questions may focus on whether there should be any limits put on science by culture and society (all the information in Issues 5, 10, 16 and 17 is relevant here). It might also be a good idea to use some of the arguments for and against censorship (Issue 20) to apply to science as well as the arts.

Specimen exam questions

AS Choose any one scientific invention or discovery that interests you and describe how it has changed society for good and/or ill.

A2 What do you understand by the term 'globalisation'? What factors (technological, economic, political) have contributed to this phenomenon?

Area 2

CULTURE, MORALITY, ARTS AND HUMANITIES

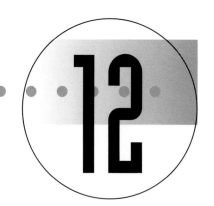

The nature of religion

Religion is one of the oldest of human activities. As far back as anthropologists (people who study the origins of humanity) can go, they find evidence of the existence of religion.

According to the *Oxford English Dictionary* (9th edition), religion is:

* the belief in a superhuman controlling power especially in a personal God or gods entitled to obedience and worship;
* the expression of this in worship;
* a particular system of faith and worship.

Major world religions

When most people use the word 'religion' they tend to use it in the third sense as the Christian religion, the Jewish religion, etc. You should be aware of the basic beliefs of each of the major world religions. All the religions have groups within them that have different interpretations or emphases (such as Catholics and Protestants in Christianity).

Buddhism

Buddhism was founded by an Indian prince, Siddhartha Gautama, known as the Buddha (the Enlightened One), in the seventh century BCE. It is based on the Four Noble Truths, which say that life is suffering and that humans are stuck on a wheel of life – they live, they die, they are reborn. Humans keep being reborn, and so suffering, because they crave life, the way out of suffering and rebirth is to follow the way of the Buddha in the Noble Eightfold Path, which, by meditation, ends craving and leads to *nirvana* (paradise). Buddhism does not necessarily involve belief in God or worship, though many Buddhists do both. The teachings of Buddhism are found in three holy books known as the *Tripitaka*.

Christianity

Christianity was founded by a Jewish teacher, Jesus of Nazareth known as the Christ (God's Anointed One), in about 30 CE. It is based on the belief that Jesus was the Son of God who showed humans what God is like. Christians believe that humans fall short of what God wants them to be and so at the end of life (Christians do not believe in reincarnation), they will not go to heaven as God wants them to. However, if they follow the Christian way of love of God and love of neighbour set out by Jesus they will spend eternity in paradise as shown in the life and resurrection of Jesus. The teachings of Christianity are found in the Bible, especially in the Gospels of the New Testament, which contain the life and teachings of Jesus.

Hinduism

Hinduism originated in India around 1500 BCE. Many Hindus say there is no such thing as Hinduism, only Hinduisms, as there are so many variations of belief. Nevertheless, there are certain beliefs most Hindus have in common. All

Hindus believe in reincarnation and karma (the law of cause and effect so that what you do in this life determines what you will be born as in your next life). They also agree that the aim of life is to escape from rebirth into *nirvana*. Different Hindu groups teach different ways to gain this freedom from rebirth, known as *moksha*. It can be achieved through fulfilling your duty as a member of a caste and so moving up the castes from the *shudras* to the *brahmins* and then to *nirvana*; through knowledge of God, through devotion to God, or through the way of yoga. Hindus believe in one universal spirit, Brahman, who is seen by humans in many different forms such as Shiva, Vishnu and Krishna. The teachings of Hinduism are found in the *Vedas*, *Upanishads*, *Ramayana* and *Bhagavad Gita*.

Islam

Muslims believe that Islam was the original religion founded by the prophet Adam at the beginning of creation, which was distorted and then given back its original form by the Prophet Muhammad in the seventh century. Muslims do not believe in reincarnation. They believe that there is only one God (who is referred to as *Allah*, the Arabic for 'the one God'). They feel that the purpose of life is to look after the world as stewards (*khalifah*) of God's creation by following the way of Islam as set out in the *Qur'an* (the word of God given directly by God to Muhammad) and in the *Sunnah* (example and sayings of Muhammad, as recorded in the *Hadith*). This way of life is the Five Pillars (belief, prayer, charity, fasting, pilgrimage) and the *Shari'ah* (the laws of Islam, which cover every aspect of life). If this way of life is followed, God will reward them with paradise after death.

Judaism

The fathers of Judaism are Abraham (1500 BCE) and Moses (1200 BCE). Jews believe in one God, who they call the Almighty because the name of God is too holy to say. They believe that God chose the Jewish people and gave his laws to the Jews so that they could be God's holy nation and bring the rest of the world to true worship of God. The laws are in the *Torah* (the first five books of the Bible) and are explained in the *Talmud* and the teachings of the *rabbis*. Jews do not believe in reincarnation, they believe that if they obey the commandments of God they will go to heaven.

Sikhism

Sikhism is based on the teachings of 10 *gurus* (teachers) and especially the first *guru*, Guru Nanak (1469–1539). It is the last of the world religions and began in the Punjab area of India, where Hindus and Muslims were fighting each other. Sikhs believe that humans are self-centred rather than God-centred, and this causes them to be reborn. So Sikhs believe in reincarnation, but they also believe that by becoming a Sikh you will not be reborn. By following the Sikh way of life of service and equality (there are no castes and no differences between men and women in Sikhism) and devotion to God, you will go to heaven. The teachings of Sikhism are found in the holy book, the *Guru Granth Sahib*.

KEY words

Agnostic someone who is not sure whether God exists

Atheist someone who believes that God does not exist

Benevolent the belief that God is all-loving and forgiving

Gurdwara a Sikh place of worship

Immortality the belief that humans have a soul that lives on forever after the death of the body

Mandir a Hindu place of worship

Monotheism the belief in one God

Mosque a Muslim place of worship

Omnipotent the belief that God is all-powerful

Omniscient the belief that God is all-knowing

Polytheism belief in many gods

Resurrection the belief that the body will come back to life at some point after death

Synagogue a Jewish place of worship

Conclusion

This survey is a definition of religions in the 'dictionary' sense. All the religions except Buddhism believe in a supreme being, God, who has created the universe. They all believe that there is a purpose in life and that by following certain rules and teachings humans will have eternity in paradise.

Sociologists study religion in its first sense and look at how it operates in society. Functionalist sociologists (see Issue 23, 'The nature of society') give a definition of religion in general, which can be useful in answering questions about the importance of religion. They claim that the key feature of religion is to answer the major and ultimate questions of that society (e.g. What is the purpose of life?) and establish a value system that unifies the members of the society. Although such a definition can be criticised because religious groups are often at the forefront of trying to change society's attitudes (e.g. Christians and the antislavery movement), it does seem that people are attracted to religion because it offers answers to the ultimate questions and gives a sense of belonging.

Symbolism and ceremony in religion

As religion is concerned with the intangible (things that cannot be tested by the senses), it uses symbolism to express ideas and beliefs that are difficult to express in straightforward language.

Some of the symbolism is in language. For Christians, the word 'father' symbolises the creativity, care and concern of God for his children; it also symbolises the relationship existing between humans and God. The word 'love' symbolises the care of God for humans, the emotions Christians should feel for God, the care and concern Christians should have for their neighbours, the relationship of God to Jesus and through Jesus to the world, etc. Some religious thinkers believe that all words used in religion are symbolic because it is impossible for anyone to describe God using human language.

Religious beliefs are also expressed symbolically in religious ceremonies and rituals. In the Christian service of the Eucharist (Holy communion), the main symbolism is the bread and wine, representative of the body and blood of Jesus. They are used to make worshippers aware of the presence of Jesus, who is regarded as an eternal spirit. The rituals of prayers and actions in a Eucharist service are intended to help the worshippers in their lives (e.g. confessing and being forgiven for sins) and to bring them into a closer relationship with God (e.g. through taking Jesus into their body through the symbols of bread and wine).

Did you know?

Would you believe it?

Numbers of religious believers worldwide (Source: *Encyclopaedia Britannica, Book of the Year* 1998)

Christians	1 929 987 000
Muslims	1 147 494 000
Buddhists	353 141 000
Hindus	746 797 000
Sikhs	22 518 000
Jews	14 890 000
World population	5 848 739 000

Numbers of religious believers in the UK (Source: *UK Christian Handbook* 1996/97)

Christians	38.2 million
Muslims	1.2 million
Buddhists	45 000
Hindus	0.4 million
Sikhs	0.6 million
Jews	0.3 million

The effects of religion on everyday life

Holding a religious belief is likely to have a huge effect on the way a person lives their life. However, it should always be remembered that people have different levels of commitment to their faith, and different members of the same faith regard different beliefs in the religion as more and less important.

Figure 12.1 Coventry Cathedral, Sutherland tapestry. What symbols can you see and what meaning might they have?

⒜ CTIVITIES

① Interview a religious believer and ask them why they believe and what effects their belief has on their way of life.

② Survey your friends to find out how many of them are atheists.

③ Use the Internet to find how many religious web sites there are.

④ Explain why some religious thinkers believe that all religious language is symbolic.

A Muslim believes that there is only one God who gave Muhammad the *Qur'an* in a form that can never be changed. This means that a Muslim must do everything the *Qur'an* says. Also, as there can be no prophets after Muhammad, Muslims must follow the example of Muhammad as set out in the *Shari'ah* (Muslim holy law). So Muslims should pray five times a day, go to mosque every Friday lunchtime, refrain from food and drink during daylight hours in Ramadan, give 2% of their wealth to the poor every year, eat only *halal* food (which means no pork or any food containing meat not slaughtered in the Muslim way), refrain from drinking alcohol, refrain from gambling, neither pay nor receive interest on loans and many, many more things. Clearly, this constitutes a major effect on life, symbolising that Islam means submission to God and a Muslim is one who has submitted to the will of God. However, not all Muslims do all of these things, because they feel that God cannot expect all of them to be followed, so they decide what are the most important and follow them; for example, some Muslims in Britain have mortgages.

Specimen exam questions

AS Examine the statement that all religions promote the same basic truths. Choose two different religions that you know well and discuss their similarities and differences.

A2 Most religions use the arts (e.g. architecture, music, painting, sculpture, poetry) to enhance worship. Illustrate this statement by detailed reference to the use of the arts in this way in any place of worship that you know well. (This question may require you to research a place of worship, e.g. Swaminariyan, Neasden, or the mosque in Regent's Park.)

13

Why people have religious belief

What is a religious belief?

It is one of the remarkable characteristics of all human beings that they claim to have religious beliefs. The word ' belief' itself can have several different meanings.

- 'Belief' might mean trust or confidence in something; for example, believing in a person or believing in justice.
- 'Belief' might mean accepting that a particular state of affairs is actually the case; for example, believing that there are tigers in India.

Religious beliefs, which can be defined as any belief that is distinctive to members of a particular religious group or denomination, are often a mixture of both types, for example:

- 'belief that' something is true, e.g. a factual proposition such as, 'Jesus was a messenger from God';
- 'belief in', which is to do with the trust and commitment people experience in their relationship with God.

Often these beliefs are interdependent. You cannot believe *in* God in the sense of trust and commitment, for example, unless you first believe *that* his existence is a fact.

Problems with religious beliefs

One of the fundamental beliefs common to most religions is the belief in some divine being or beings. In the modern world this belief raises serious problems. How can someone claim that some special knowledge or message that he or she believes they have received from God is real knowledge? How do we know, for example, that *Mother Theresa* or *St Francis of Assisi* were not mistaken about their belief that God spoke to them? We cannot prove the existence of God by either rational or empirical means – the two generally acceptable methods of establishing proof of the existence of something.

Types of knowledge

Particularly since the work of *René Descartes* (1596–1650), a *rationalist* philosopher, there has been a strong tradition arguing that to know something is to be able to prove it: to reach a conclusion by logical inferences from self-evident premises. In practice, this means proving things by using your reason; for example, proving that 2 + 2 = 4 or proving Pythagoras' theorem. However, *rational knowledge* cannot tell us anything about the real world. *Empirical knowledge*, on the other hand, is based on sense-experience, our perceptions of the real world. But the problem with sense-experiences is that they may be mistaken. For example, railway lines appear to converge in the distance even though they are actually parallel. So rational knowledge is certain knowledge, but it is only about logic, and empirical knowledge is about the real world, but it may be mistaken. Religious believers usually claim that their religious beliefs are *real* but are not simply matters of logic or ideas, or mistaken sense – impressions.

Where do religious beliefs come from?

There are various answers to this question including the religious, the sociological and the psychological.

Religious explanations

Many religious believers would claim that their religious belief is based on a *religious experience*, which led to their *conversion*. Conversion often involves a dramatic change of attitude, beliefs and behaviour. The best known example of this is *Paul* on the road to Damascus, who changed suddenly from being a prosecutor of the early Christian Church into its greatest missionary after experiencing a blinding light and hearing a voice. The problem for religious believers is that they are usually certain about their beliefs and they want to claim when they say, for example, that 'Jesus is the Son of God', that this is a real state of affairs.

Other religious experiences might take the form of an appearance by a saint or a divine figure, hearing voices or experiencing some strange phenomena, such as:

- Moses and the burning bush;
- the Virgin Mary appearing to Bernadette of Lourdes;
- the angel Gabriel appearing to the prophet Muhammad.

However, it is difficult to establish the authenticity of these events by the usual methods. Also, the claim that a particular experience is an experience of God may simply be self-deception. The experience may be self-generated, i.e. arise in the imagination of the person having the experience, rather than having been caused by a source outside.

Peter Sutcliffe, '*the Yorkshire Ripper*,' claimed that God told him to murder 14 women. Joan of Arc claimed that the saints spoke to her and told her to save France. It is extremely difficult to prove or disprove the authenticity of these claims as they are intensely personal, private, 'inner' experiences, which, by their very nature, cannot be shared.

Some religious believers claim that their belief is based on a religious book, such as the Bible or the *Qur'an*. This raises several problems.

- Some passages in these religious texts seem to contradict each other.
- It is often not clear whether particular passages have divine or human origins, despite the claims made by some believers that their scriptures are inspired by God (see 'Did you know? box').

Did you know?

Bible notes

- In the southern USA there are small groups of Christians who handle rattle snakes during their services. This is based on an interpretation of Mark 16:18, which most biblical scholars regard as a later addition.

- In the book of Joshua, Ch. 7, the ancient Israelites slaughtered all the inhabitants of Jericho because they thought this would be pleasing to God. In Matthew 5–7, Jesus taught that you should love your enemies.

- Most Jehovah's Witnesses and Mormons give up at least 10% of their income to their church.

- Many religious believers belong to small cults and sects, which often have very extreme views and powerful influential leaders. Some of these expected the end of the world and/or the return of Jesus Christ at the end of the second millennium.

- Most religious texts reflect the social/cultural conditions of their own time and it can be difficult to see how they can be the basis of religious faith 2000 years later.
- Only one religious book can be true and there is no way of deciding which it is.

Sociological explanations for religious belief (see also Issue 14, 'The need for morality and the nature of ethical theories')

Sociological theories tend to assume that the explanation for religious belief lies in society itself, rather than in the idea that there is some external divine reality responsible for the experiences that believers claim to have had. Sociologists are interested in *belief systems* rather than individual beliefs, because most religious believers have an interlocking set of beliefs, rather than individual ones. They are also interested in the way in which religious beliefs reflect and are part of the *culture* of a particular society. Indian children are more likely to be Hindus than European children because their religious beliefs have been learnt within a Hindu culture. In 1912 the French sociologist *Emile Durkheim* offered a *functionalist* analysis of religion in terms of what purposes religion serves in society. These include:

- *Social solidarity.* Social life is impossible without shared values and moral beliefs. Religion reinforces those values and collective religious worship is a way of bringing people together so that they can integrate and strengthen the moral values that unite them.
- *Reverence for society.* Durkheim argued that when people have the experience of standing before the divine or some greater power, what they are really doing is worshipping society itself. People use religious ideas as a symbol of what they hold most sacred, which is the tribe or clan and its values and customs to which they belong.

There are other functions of religious belief identified by sociologists.

- *Crisis management.* Religious belief and ritual helps people to deal with life crises such as birth, puberty, marriage and death. The religious services surrounding such events help people to cope with the disruption of their lives caused by such things as death and to support each other. This support helps to reintegrate society and to provide solidarity.
- *Meaning of life.* Religion also helps people to cope with uncertainty in life. It helps them to answer the difficult questions like why there is evil and suffering and whether there is life after death.
- *Continuity.* Religious ceremonies help to maintain a sense of history and link together different generations.

Critics have pointed out however, that if religious belief is merely a reinforcement and reflection of the values of society as a whole, it is hard to see where revolutionaries or prophets come from in the first place. If religion were no more than a reflection of society's values, the ability to criticise the values of the society in which they have grown up or to develop a more universal perspective on life would never have developed.

Psychological explanations for religious belief

Sigmund Freud (1856–1939), the originator of psychoanalysis, regarded religious beliefs as 'illusions, fulfilments of the oldest, strongest and most insistent wishes of mankind'. He regarded them as a mental defence against the more threatening aspects of nature, floods, death and disease, etc. According to Freud, human beings project onto the universe the memory of their father as a great projecting power in order to cope with the threat of these natural forces. Although much of Freud's explanation is rejected by modern critics, his view of religious belief as a kind of 'psychological crutch' is accepted by many religious thinkers as a true description of some aspects of religion.

Karl Marx (1818–1883) described religion as 'the opiate of the masses'. As an atheist, he argued that there is no God except the God that man creates for himself. Religious belief encourages human beings to put up with intolerable conditions and obscures the fact that history is controlled by human interests and desires. Religion does not help human beings, but chains them.

Figure 13.1 Hindus bathing in The Ganges – many religions see water as purifying sin and bringing people closer to God

ACTIVITIES

① Research the life of Jackie Pullinger in Hong Kong or Camillo Torres in Colombia. What effect do you think their religious beliefs have had on their lives?

② Religious beliefs are an essential part of a society's culture. What evidence is there to support or oppose this point of view?

③ 'Religious beliefs do not have to be true. They just have be important to the believer.' Evaluate this statement, giving reasons for your answer.

Conclusion

It does not follow necessarily that the modern criticisms of religious belief have destroyed its meaning. Religion is a complex set of beliefs and activities, some of which are open to attack. However, it is just as difficult to disprove religious beliefs, such as the existence of God, as it is to prove them.

Specimen exam questions

AS   Examine the view that all religions serve the same spiritual and social purpose and promote the same basic values. Discuss this view in relation to two different religions with which you are familiar.

A2   'If God did not exist, it would be necessary to invent Him.' What do you think Voltaire meant by this statement and what relevance does it have in the twenty-first century?

14

The need for morality and the nature of ethical theories

Why morality is important

Human beings are gregarious – they like to be with other people and they like to live in groups or societies. If you live in a society, then you need to know how other people are likely to act, and you need some method of balancing one person's self-interest against the self-interests of others.

A set of moral principles is known as a moral code. Sociologists sometimes call this 'a shared value system'. They feel that any society needs to have shared values if it is to survive, because without shared values there will be conflict.

As societies have come together and changed, there can be several value systems at work and this is why there is now debate about moral issues. There are no longer shared values about issues such as cohabitation (living together without being married), divorce, abortion, fighting for your country, etc.

Even though there are such differences about what is right and what is wrong, we all make moral judgements saying, 'this is right' or 'that is wrong'. In fact, we have to do this. If you are offered drugs, if your boyfriend/girlfriend wants you to sleep with them, you have to make a moral choice. If you are a scientist cloning sheep, or a doctor killing human embryos in order to give a couple a baby through IVF, you are making a moral decision. Studying ethics should help you to make informed moral choices and moral judgements.

KEY words

Amoral outside morality, or having no moral principles

Conscience an inner feeling about good and bad, which makes you feel you ought to do the good and makes you feel guilty if you do the bad

Consequential an ethical theory, which says that what makes an act good or bad is the effects or consequences of the action

Deontological an ethical theory based on rules rather than the effects of an action, which says some things are absolutely right and others are absolutely wrong

Duty following your conscience by doing what you feel you ought to do

Immoral having moral principles, but going against them

Objective morality an ethical theory based on outside facts, which are independent of an individual

Subjective morality an ethical theory based on the ideas of an individual

Ethical theories

There are many different theories on what makes an action right or wrong. You should use at least some of these theories when you are answering questions on ethical issues in the exam.

Utilitarianism

This is the view that you decide whether an action is right or wrong by looking at the consequences. If you have a choice of actions, you should choose the one that will produce the most happiness or the least suffering to the people who will be affected by the action. For example, if you had to decide whether to ban smoking in public places, you would weigh the suffering caused to the smokers by having to wait for a cigarette against the suffering caused to non-smokers by passive smoking (lung cancer, heart disease, bronchial problems, etc.) and decide that the least suffering would be caused by banning smoking.

This theory is associated with *Jeremy Bentham* (1748–1832) and *John Stuart Mill* (1806–1873) and the phrase 'a good action is one that brings about the greatest happiness of the greatest number'.

Religious morality

Almost all religions argue that it is God who decides what is right and what is wrong and that humans discover how to behave from finding out God's will. Christians believe that this comes from the teachings of the Bible and the decisions of the Church. Muslims believe that God's will was revealed through the *Qur'an* and the Prophet Muhammad and from these Muslim lawyers have worked out the *Shari'ah*, a holy law covering every aspect of life. So, if Muslims are faced with a moral choice, they find out what the *Shari'ah* says. Orthodox Jews consult the laws of God found in the *Torah* (the first five books of the Old Testament). Buddhists would look at the moral precepts laid down by the Buddha. In all these cases, there is no looking at consequences, what makes something right or wrong is decided by God.

So, if faced with the issue of whether homosexuals should be allowed to marry, Christians would look at the Bible and say that homosexuality is condemned, therefore homosexuality is wrong and there can be no marriage. A Muslim would make a similar statement, based on the teachings of the *Qur'an*.

However, not all religious people would make moral decisions in this way. Many feel that the consequences must be looked at and that some of the laws in the holy books were only intended for the time when they were written. If two people love each other and want to commit themselves to each other in marriage, then allowing them to do so is the most loving thing, so homosexual marriage should be allowed.

Did you know?

Freewill and determinism

All morality and all laws are based on the idea that human beings have freewill –they can make choices and could have behaved in a different way from the way they did behave.

However, some scientists argue for determinism – the idea that all actions have scientific causes, which humans are not free to alter. Just as water boils if it is heated, so a person with a certain type of genetic character and a certain type of upbringing will steal. This means that all human actions are determined by what has happened to them and that it is therefore impossible to make moral choices.

'There is an inescapable sense that events are somehow influenced by human choice. Without that, there would be no sense of morality.' (Mel Thompson, *Teach Yourself Ethics*, 1994)

Natural law

Thomas Aquinas (1224–1274) used the earlier work of Aristotle to claim that just as there are natural laws of science, so there is a natural law of morality. Just as scientists can study the world and find the principles on which it is based, so moral philosophers can study humans and society and find out what is the 'natural' form of behaviour, which will lead to a perfect society if everyone follows it.

Aquinas believed that God created everything with a final cause or purpose and that discovering this tells you what is right. For example the final cause of sex is the creation of children, so any form of sex that does not involve the creation of children is wrong. Those who follow natural law today tend to relate behaviour to the place of humans in the world and the basic requirements for humans to survive.

To take another example, if making a decision about homosexual marriage, they would say that heterosexuality is natural because it is a basic requirement for humans to survive and so homosexuality must be wrong and homosexual marriage cannot be allowed.

Selfish laws?

In his book, *A Theory of Justice*, John Rawls, a US professor of law suggested that to decide on moral principles and laws we should put ourselves into a situation where we know all about the world (that it's better to be white, male middle-class, living in the West, etc., even though most people in the world are black, poor and living in the developing world), but we do not know who we are going to be in the world. He called this, 'the original position'. He claimed that this would make us want laws to protect human rights (freedom of religion, freedom of speech, the right to vote, the right to hold office, etc.), laws that would share out the world's resources and moral principles fairly and so encourage people to help the less fortunate.

Rawls was criticised because all these ideas are based on selfishness – we would want the laws and morals out of self-interest in case we were poor or black or female, etc. Is it wrong to base morality on self-interest?

Social contract theory

This is a view first put forward by Plato, but very much connected with *Thomas Hobbes* (1588–1679) and *Jean-Jaques Rousseau* (1712–1778). It claims that laws and morals are a human invention upon which we agree to make life better for ourselves. As Hobbes said, 'Life without laws would be nasty, brutish and short.' Rousseau claimed that if governments or rulers do not make life better for their subjects, then the subjects have a right to overthrow the government.

If making a decision about homosexuality, social contract theorists would say, 'What would be the impact on society? Is it something like adultery, which we can't have laws about without being too restrictive on people's freedom?' They would then probably agree to homosexual marriage because it will make the couple more stable and therefore make society more stable.

① Make a list of as many arguments as you can in favour of cloning animals. Make a list of as many arguments as you can against cloning animals. Read the key words list on deontological and consequential. Go through your lists and work out which of your arguments are deontological and which are consequential. Do you think your lists make you agree or disagree with cloning?

② Look at the 'Did You Know?' box. If there are five billion people in the world and three billion are women and one billion live in the West, what is the probability that you will be a male living in the West? (Use your GCSE Maths probability and multiply the probabilities.)

Make a list of the morals and laws you would put forward if you were in Rawls' 'original position'. Are they similar to those Rawls suggests? Write down what you think of Rawls' ideas and why.

③ Read through the section on 'Ethical theories' and using the key word definitions of 'objective' and 'subjective', work out which theories are objective and which are subjective.

Read through 'Ethical theories' again using the key word definitions of 'deontological' and 'consequential' and work out which theories are deontological and which are consequential.

Decide which theory you would find most useful in making a moral decision and why.

⑤ Use the Internet to discover a country with a high population growth. Also find out its gross national product (GNP) and per capita income. Then use the ethical theories and your own ideas to discuss whether the country should adopt a policy of compulsory sterilisation for couples after they have had one baby. Remember that 'discuss' requires looking at arguments for and against and coming to a conclusion on the basis of the evidence you have put forward.

⑤ On the basis of all the work you have done, answer the question

'Is it ever justifiable to break the law?'. You may find it useful to go through each ethical theory and work out a situation where the people who follow that type of ethical theory might feel justified in breaking the law. You must give reasons for each example and come to a conclusion based on what you have said.

You should word-process your answer and save it on disc.

CULTURE, MORALITY, ARTS AND HUMANITIES

Figure 14.1 Making moral decisions

Specimen exam questions

AS   Outline the various factors that contribute to our notions of 'right' and 'wrong' and the way we behave individually and in groups. To what extent is it possible to tolerate differences of opinion about such matters?

A2   Illustrate with appropriate examples what connections exist between religious belief, morality and the law and how they exert different influences on the ways in which people behave.

15

Rights and responsibilities

According to the *Oxford English Dictionary*, the word 'right', means 'a justifiable claim on legal or moral grounds to have or obtain something or to act in a certain way'. The question of rights can be interpreted in different ways; it can be analysed from a philosophical, moral, legal or political point of view. Many modern discussions of rights and responsibilities are a response to political situations where human rights appear to be absent. These include:

- minority rights – concerned with the way religious or ethnic groups are treated;
- gay rights – concerned with discrimination against homosexuals;
- women's rights – concerned with the role and rights of women in society, particularly in relation to less developed countries;
- animal rights – concerned with the treatment of animals, particularly in relation to hunting, conservation and animal experimentation.

The issue of rights only arises because human beings tend to live in communities and there are often conflicts between the interests of individuals. On a desert island with only one human being present, there are no such conflicts. The status of rights is often categorised as one of the following:

- *Legal rights*. An example of a legal right would be the right of ownership to legally acquired property. This type of right can be protected by law. Legal rights also involve the right to behave in a certain way or to expect someone else to do so, such as a legally binding contract requiring someone to supply certain services in exchange for money.
- *Moral rights*. The right of an old person to care and respect is an example of a moral right, although this would not be directly enforceable in law. Similarly, one might argue for the rights of an unborn child and against the rights of the mother to choose in the context of a possible abortion. Whatever the legal status of the act of abortion itself, there is still a further moral discussion about rights involved.
- *Universal rights*. This category would include those rights with a possible moral basis but which are not necessarily legally supported in some countries or societies. For example, most people would argue that no human being should be a slave and that this right of freedom should apply universally, or that people should have the right to free speech, to express their opinions in public without fear of persecution. In practice, rights often take the form of:
  - *claims*: being owed money means that you have a claim on the debtor;
  - *powers*: the right to distribute your property in your will;
  - *liberties*: being exempt from giving evidence against a spouse in court;
  - *immunities*: the right not to be persecuted for joining a trade union.

The origins of human rights

Article 1 of the *Universal Declaration of Human Rights* produced by the United Nations in 1948 states, 'All human beings are born free and equal in dignity and rights. They are endowed with reason and conscience and should act towards each other in a spirit of brotherhood.' The Declaration goes on to specify a long list of human rights including the rights to life, liberty and security, freedom from slavery and freedom of movement across national borders. Although most civilised societies would agree to this declaration, at least in theory, there have been different views in the history of thought concerning exactly what rights human beings should have, and the basis on which such rights can be justified.

Natural rights and natural law

The phrase 'human rights' is comparatively recent. Traditionally, the phrase 'natural rights' was used and this was often based on natural law. This refers to the idea that all people recognise some moral obligation, which gives rise to generally agreed moral principles. The classical Greek philosophers, Socrates, Plato and Aristotle all argued that there is a natural justice or a right thing to do.

- In the New Testament, *Paul* spoke of those who obey by nature the things of the law, because they have the law written on their conscience (Romans, 11).
- *Thomas Aquinas* (1224–1274) linked Christian belief with the idea of natural law in the thirteenth century. He argued that there are certain principles of true morality and justice discernible by human reason without the aid of revelation (even though they are of divine origin). Manmade laws that conflict with these principles are not valid law.
- *Thomas Hobbes* (1588–1679) argued that in its natural state, human life was 'solitary, poor, nasty, brutish and short'. In order to protect people from one another, a 'social contract' was needed, which involved the natural right not to be harmed by another.
- *John Locke* (1632–1704) had a more optimistic view of human nature. Human beings are naturally capable of acting in the interests of others and of recognising a natural law, instituted by God, which says that 'no one should harm another in his life, health, liberty or possessions'.
- The *American Declaration of Independence* (1776) is another example. It claimed to be founded on the self-evident truths that man has a right to life, liberty and the pursuit of happiness.

However, the Utilitarian philosopher, *Jeremy Bentham* (1748–1832) argued that there was no such thing as human rights. His theory was designed to cut through all the confusion and conflicts to which arguing about human rights might lead. He believed that the assertion of natural rights incites 'selfish and dissocial passions', the great enemies of public peace, and so militates against social order and the laws of the land. Human rights were not something to which human beings were entitled by right of being human, but only permissible if they contributed more happiness than unhappiness to society.

Article 18 of the *Universal Declaration of Human Rights* states that everyone has the 'right to freedom of thought, conscience and religion'. It could be suggested that this is the part of the declaration that has been most flagrantly ignored and contravened since the Second World War. All over the world, the right to express political or religious views contradicting those of the prevailing authorities has been removed and those expressing such views have been imprisoned, expelled, tortured and/or killed. Examples include:

- the murder of thousands of *Baha'is* (a pacifist religion) in Iran in the 1980s;
- the obliteration of Tibetan Buddhist culture after the Chinese invasion;
- the torture of men, women and children in Bosnia in the1990s;
- the struggle for independence by the Kurds against, Iraq, Turkey and Russia.

Did you know?

Moral responsibilities

- At least five different British companies provide electronic torture equipment such as cattle prods to repressive regimes.
- Official Roman Catholic teaching regards contraception as a sin because it is against their understanding of natural law.
- In 1998, at least 5000 people died in 114 countries from torture or imprisonment.
- During the 1999 World Trade Talks, some less developed countries objected to the idea of abolishing child or slave labour.

KEY words

Amnesty International a voluntary organisation founded in 1961, which publicises and fights for the freedom of people who are unfairly imprisoned, tortured and otherwise persecuted for speaking out against corruption

Homophobia an extreme aversion to and prejudice against the idea and practice of homosexual relationships of either sex

Justice refers to the idea of fairness and equality for all and to the system of reward and punishment that helps to maintain it

Sexism the view that one sex (usually women) is inferior emotionally, intellectually or physically and the practical application of this attitude in society

Speciesism the view that animals have fewer rights than human beings and could be used for such things as experiments

Responsibilities

The idea of responsibility can refer to the idea that people are answerable for their behaviour, implying that they are free to choose their actions and can thus be praised or blamed for what they actually do (see Issue 25, 'The nature of law'). But it can also refer to the idea of 'duty'. Duty can be defined as 'the obligation of an individual to satisfy a claim made upon him by the community or individual or group in order to serve the common good'. In all successful societies, rights and duties have to be balanced against each other. If children have a legal and/or moral right to education, then the parents and the state have a duty to provide it. Another good example of this balance can be seen in the purchase and use of a railway ticket. The railway company has the duty to convey the passenger from one place to another and has the right to be paid for doing so. The passenger has the duty to pay for this ticket and the right to be conveyed to the destination for which they have paid.

This relationship between rights and duties has given rise to the view that all morality depends on a '*social contract*'. Individuals agree to perform certain duties in exchange for the acquisition of certain rights. For example, law-abiding citizens agree to respect the property of their neighbours, in exchange for the right to have their own property protected.

Figure 15.1 Conflict of rights – these protestors feel they have the right to deny homosexuals rights

What is our duty?

The philosopher *Immanuel Kant* (1724–1804) argued that human beings are rational and have the capacity to work out what their duty is and to do it. For Kant, a good action is one that involves doing what you ought to do, rather than what you want to do. Reason tells you that you ought always to treat people as ends in themselves, rather than as means to an end. This involves always telling the truth and never taking life.

The Ten Commandments

Some lists of duties such as the Ten Commandments have stood the test of time. Whatever their religious inspiration, they seem to contain basic rules that contribute to the survival of civilised human communities. Basic human rights seem to be protected when people accept the following duties:

- Do not steal.
- Do not commit adultery.
- Do not tell lies.
- Do not kill.
- Honour your father and mother.

The problem with duties

The problem with lists of duties, however, is that they never allow for exceptional circumstances. There are always situations, for example, where one might consider that killing in self-defence or lying about the whereabouts of a relation being pursued by an assassin seems to be the right course of action. However, in general, discussing human behaviour in terms of rights and duties seems to contribute positively towards the preservation of society.

Specimen exam questions

AS To what extent is there opportunity for all in Britain today? How far is equality of opportunity a desirable or achievable ideal?

A2 Examine critically the aims and effects of government initiatives on *two* of the following: race; gender; age or disability.

ACTIVITIES

① Should human rights only be granted to those people who carry out their duties to others? Give examples to support your views.

② 'Whatever is my right as a man (woman) is also the right of another and it becomes my duty to guarantee as well as to possess.' (Thomas Paine). How far do you think that this idea could be used to support the criticism of another country's human rights record and why?

③ What effective measures do you think could taken by members of a society in order to guarantee and maintain basic human rights?

16

Abortion

A bortion is defined as 'a premature expulsion of the foetus from the womb procured by a doctor'. It is a highly emotive subject, about which many groups of people have very strong feelings. In order to discuss it knowledgeably, you need to know the following:

• the legal position concerning abortion
• the scientific/medical evidence concerning the status of the foetus
• the ethical and/or religious reasons influencing the views held by individuals and groups.

There are three issues central to the abortion debate.

• Should a woman have the right to do what she wants with her own body?
• Does a foetus have the same rights as someone who is already living independently?
• Is a foetus a person?

In an ideal world, these issues would not arise. However, the reality of human life forces people to make difficult decisions. Most religious and moral views agree that, in principle, human life is sacred. However, they differ in how far they are prepared to put aside this principle in particular circumstances. The Roman Catholic Church, for example, tends to take a very strong view on this issue. It would not allow abortion on the grounds of rape or incest, but would allow it if it were clear that the mother would definitely die otherwise. This is the *natural law position* – the idea that human life is sacred and that pregnancy and the creation of human life are natural processes and ultimately part of God's will and the natural order of things. Hence, any interference with this process is against God's will. (This argument also would also apply to issues such as contraception and euthanasia.) However, you could argue that the Roman Catholic position is rather biased because it seems to assume that its own interpretation of what is God's will and the natural order of things is the only correct one. One could argue that taking a painkiller to relieve a headache is also interference with a natural process, but the results of this interference are obviously less lethal in the case of the headache.

Objections to abortion often seem to concentrate exclusively on the act of abortion itself and to ignore the circumstances in which an abortion was considered. This raises the question of whether actions should be judged by the result they produce or by the motives from which they were done. This can be difficult to decide. For example, how would you assess the result of an abortion if it took away the life of the unborn child but made the mother happy?

Some churches and other organisations would allow abortion in cases of rape, incest or where bringing the pregnancy to full term would seriously damage the health or threaten the life of the mother, or where the deformity of the foetus precludes any chance of survival.

Did you know?

• Since the 1967 Abortion Act there have been five million abortions in the UK.

• Five hundred abortions are performed each day in the UK.

• In 1968 there were 22 000 abortions; in 1998 there were 177 000.

• Ninety-one per cent of abortions in 1998 were carried out because of a risk to the mental or physical health of the mother.

• Sixty-six per cent of women who have abortions are single.

• 'Directly willed and procured abortions are to be absolutely excluded as a means of regulating birth.' (Pope Paul VI, *Humanae Vitae*, 1968)

How may the rights of the mother be balanced against the rights of the unborn child?

Many moral issues seem to centre on the problem of competing rights. Those opposed to the 1967 Abortion Act have argued amongst other things, that the phrase 'risk to the physical or mental health of the mother' is too vague and allows abortions to be granted for trivial and irresponsible reasons. If abortion involves the taking away of human life, then the argument that the mother doesn't want the child, or can't support it, is not sufficient to justify it. There are far more couples waiting to adopt new-born babies than there are babies available for adoption. This argument implies that the risk to the health of the mother is not equal to the death of the baby. In terms of rights, what is being said is that the right of the mother to decide to have an abortion in these cases is not as great as the right of the unborn child to live. Many of those opposed to abortion itself, see themselves as defending the rights of a foetus, which cannot defend itself.

From the moral point of view, it is usually agreed that rights and responsibilities go together. Some people have argued, for example, that a couple or a single person leading a totally promiscuous lifestyle who ignore readily available contraceptive techniques should not be allowed to choose an abortion, which involves the death of a human being and the use of expensive, hard-pressed NHS resources.

Exercising the right to choose an abortion denies the right of a foetus to live. So the freedom to make decisions carries with it the responsibility to make these decisions carefully and sensitively, as human life is involved.

KEY words

Embryo the organism between 14 days and the eighth week of gestation

Foetus the developing human being between 14 weeks and birth

Pro-choice the term used by those who consider that a woman's right to choose is absolute

Pro-life the term used by those who argue that a foetus is an innocent human being, who should never be killed

Personhood consciousness, the ability to feel pain, a developed capacity for reasoning, the ability to communicate and self-awareness (Dr. Mary Warren)

Viability the term used to describe the independent survival of a foetus outside the womb

Zygote the cell formed by the union of sperm and ovum

Is a foetus a human being in the same sense that we apply the term to human beings outside the womb?

Foetuses rarely survive *ex utero* (outside the womb) before 22 weeks. (The fact that some do survive at this early stage has been important evidence in favour of the recent amendment to the 1967 Abortion Act, passed by parliament in 1990, reducing the maximum time for an abortion from 28 weeks to 24 weeks). Many doctors, nurses and others involved in the operation of abortion, pointed out that at 26 weeks, for example, an aborted foetus could be left to die, while a

Figure 16.1 A foetus at 20 weeks

ACTIVITIES

① Read the following statements:
  a) A foetus is not really a human being.
  b) Abortion is just another form of birth control.
  c) Abortion stops the birth of unwanted children.
  d) Legalised abortion stops the misery and exploitation of young girls trying to conceal or escape from their pregnancy.
  e) Abortion must be allowed in the case of rape.
  On your own, write either 'true', 'false' or 'not sure' after each of the above statements. Then compare your answers with someone else, noting those where you agreed and disagreed.
  Pick one of the statements about which you have strong views. Write down the evidence and any other points you would use to convince someone who disagreed with you. How much of your argument is based on fact? How much is based on strong personal feelings?

② Using an example from any recent television series you may have watched, discuss the difficulties faced by someone thinking about abortion.

③ Why is abortion described as an issue about competing rights?

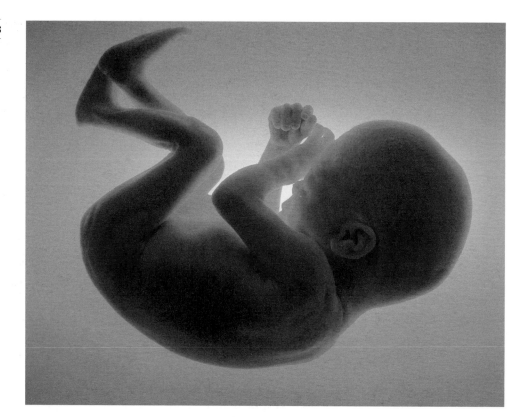

younger premature baby could legally only receive life-enhancing treatment, even though the doctors had decided that he/she had virtually no chance of long-term survival. The dependence of the foetus on the womb for survival before this time is often used as evidence that the foetus is not fully human. However, this dependence on outside sources for survival extends far longer than the period in the womb. Being born and expelled from the womb is not a true test of independence.

Conclusion

The decision to afford a potential human being the same status as an existing human being does safeguard the rights of an unborn child. But these rights have to be balanced against the rights of the potential mother to decide what to do with her own body and the fact that the discomfort of pregnancy and the pain and risk of childbirth can only be experienced by her in a personal way. There is no right answer but the action that tries to produce the greatest good in the circumstances may be the best that anyone can do.

Specimen exam questions

AS   Summarise the arguments that can be presented both for *and* against abortion.

A2   Do you think abortion is an issue that should be decided by law or left to the individual mother? Give reasons for your answer.

17

Euthanasia

Euthanasia is a compound of two Greek words – *eu* and *thanatos* – meaning literally 'a good death'. The word is generally understood today to refer to the 'mercy killing' of a person by another, either with or without the person's consent. There are two important features to remember about euthanasia.

- It involves taking someone's life.
- It is done for the claimed benefit of the person whose life is being taken, usually because he/she is suffering from an incurable or terminal illness.

Historically, all civilised societies have moral principles about the taking of human life, but there have been considerable variations concerning when it is permissible. Infanticide and suicide were all accepted and widely practised in Greek and Roman times. However, the growth in influence of Judaism and Christianity in the western world led to the view that human life was sacred and only God had the power to take it.

Euthanasia and the law

At the moment, euthanasia is illegal in this country. Despite fairly recent bills debated in the House of Lords in 1969 and 1976 in support of it, the bills were defeated, mainly on the grounds that it seemed to be too difficult to draw up adequate safeguards to protect a possible recipient of euthanasia from unfair pressure or abuse. However in 1993, the Dutch parliament made law certain guidelines under which doctors could carry on administering lethal injections to consenting, terminally ill and suffering patients without fear of prosecution – a practice in which some Dutch doctors had already been engaged for several years.

Modern life-support systems make such decisions very difficult. The initial positive decision by a doctor to place someone on a life-support machine in order to improve the chances of survival, may become a more controversial issue under the following circumstances:

- removing someone when there is no possibility of improvement;
- removing someone when life is only being maintained by the machine, e.g. a serious brain-stem injury;
- removing a seriously deformed and/or very premature baby.

Without modern life-support machines, the question of survival for the examples mentioned above, would not arise. However, a doctor can now be sued for switching off a machine, an action which is seen as life-threatening or life-taking. On the other hand, without the opportunity of being on the machine in the first place, the patient would certainly have died. Medical ethics often discusses these issues in terms of *proportionality*. This involves balancing the amount of benefit accruing to the patient in relation to the amount of pain, suffering, cost, inconvenience, etc.

What is death?

A modern philosopher, Peter Singer, has argued that the growth of our capacity to keep people alive has forced us to reconsider what we mean by 'the sanctity of life' and what we mean by death. It is now generally accepted that *brain-stem death* (when there is no chance of the brain recovering the use of its functions) is real death. This means that bodies that appear to be warm, pulsating and breathing are technically dead, and will be given no further medical support, but may be kept functioning until vital organs can be removed for transplants.

Case studies

Baby John was born prematurely at 27 weeks with an infection and breathing difficulties and placed on a ventilator, initially for a month. However, he remained very ill and handicapped, suffered from convulsions and breathing problems, which did not improve. His long-term prospects for a reasonable quality of life were described as non-existent. He was severely brain-damaged, blind and deaf and in constant pain (*The Independent*, 23 October 1990).

In a court case, the judge ruled that the baby should be treated with antibiotics for his chest infection but that his doctors were not obliged to put him back on the ventilator.

This decision was based on two principles:

- It would not serve the child's best interests to give him treatment that would prolong his suffering and produce no benefit.
- There is a difference between normal care – antibiotics – and extraordinary care – life support machines.

In September 1992, Dr Cox was found guilty of deliberately killing a 70-year-old patient, Mrs Boyes, who was terminally ill with rheumatoid arthritis, in terrible pain and who had asked Dr Cox to help her die. Mrs Boyes could not be relieved from her pain or cured and the injection given to her by Dr Cox was deliberately designed to end her life.

The court ruled that Dr Cox's action was illegal because it was 'deliberately designed to take a life.'

Tony Bland was in 'a persistent vegetative state' from 1989 until 1992 after the Hillsborough football disaster. His body continued to function but there was no possibility of the recovery of consciousness because of his severe brain damage.

The court ruled that doctors could discontinue ventilation, nutrition and hydration by artificial means.

According to Michael Keeling, a writer on Christian ethics, these three cases raise many of the difficult questions surrounding euthanasia, for example, deciding which of the following actions is legally or morally permissible:

- withdrawing sustenance, which will inevitably lead to death (Tony Bland)
- not using 'extraordinary' or disproportionate care to keep a baby alive where the cost or difficulty of the care outweighs the possible benefit (Baby John).

KEY words

Involuntary euthanasia ending someone's life when they have not given consent but were able to do so

Non-voluntary euthanasia ending the life of someone who cannot choose for themselves

Voluntary euthanasia helping someone to die at their own request

Active euthanasia a positive action that brings about death – it can apply to all three types of euthanasia mentioned above

Disproportionate treatment treatment that may involve so much invasive surgery, cost or pain that the possible benefit is insignificant in proportion

Passive euthanasia a lack of action, which will bring about death –may also apply to the three types of euthanasia mentioned above

Arguments for euthanasia

- Mature human beings should have the right to choose what to do with their own lives.
- Human beings should have the right to end a life that may consist only of pain, incurable illness, loss of dignity, dependence on others and loneliness.
- Euthanasia avoids the situation of being a constant physical, emotional and financial burden on others.

The points mentioned above refer to *voluntary euthanasia*, where the patient can choose for him/herself. When a patient is in a coma, so seriously ill that they are incapable of making a decision or in the case of an incurably sick baby in an incubator, then someone else has to choose to terminate their life. This is known as *involuntary euthanasia*. This raises the problem that the responsibility for the death now lies with someone else and also the problem of how you stop a helpless patient from being murdered by greedy relatives who then claim that they were carrying out the wishes of the victim. In Holland, they have introduced the idea of 'a living will', a legal document prepared in advance, which states clearly what is to be done if the patient becomes incapacitated.

Figure 17.1 Dr Kevorkian (right) with the relative of a patient whom he helped to commit suicide

Did you know?

To die a dignified death?

In May 1995, the Legislative Assembly of The Northern Territories Of Australia became the first parliament to legalise voluntary euthanasia.

In May 1994, in Michigan, USA, Dr Jack Kevorkian ('Dr Death') was acquitted of taking the life of one of the many patients he had helped to commit suicide. He had invented a machine called the Mercitron, which allowed patients to kill themselves painlessly and he advertised his services in newspapers. He was stripped of his medical licence.

Arguments against euthanasia

- Voluntary euthanasia has been condemned by many church and civil organisations, including the *World Medical Association*.
- Where euthanasia is legal, compulsory termination of life has been used by some governments, such as Nazi Germany, to remove those who embarrassed the state, either through political opposition or because of so-called racial, mental, physical or social deficiencies.
- The practice of euthanasia would undermine the trust that patients have in the medical profession always acting in the interests of preserving life.
- If you allow exceptions to the principle that human life is sacred, you weaken the principle itself.
- The evidence gained from the hospice movement in the past few years has also shown that people can experience terminal illnesses in a context of love, dignity and painlessness, surrounded by their family. This evidence attacks the view that euthanasia is preferable to letting a terminal illness take its natural course.
- Many religious people would argue that because the right to life is God-given, the value of human beings is constant, whether rich or poor, strong or weak, handicapped or normal. No human life can be sacrificed merely for the economic or political welfare of either states or individuals. However, individuals may decide to sacrifice themselves in exceptional circumstances. It is never permissible to take innocent life.

Conclusion

The increase in the number of old people in the population and the increasing sophistication of life-support machines has made the issue of legalising euthanasia very important. If human life is sacred, in principle, are there any circumstances where the taking of life can be justified?

Specimen exam questions

A CTIVITIES

① What arguments would you use to defend/oppose the actions of the doctors in the cases described in the above case studies?

② Discuss the view that the legalisation of euthanasia would put unfair pressure on doctors and incurably ill elderly patients.

③ Should the decision to end someone's life be a medical or a moral decision and who should be involved?

AS 'Everyone has the right to an easy death.' Evaluate the arguments both for *and* against this statement.

A2 'Life is sacred and no one has the right to take it, not even on their own.' Consider both the strengths and weaknesses of this viewpoint.

18

Aesthetic evaluation

Baroque seventeenth- and eighteenth-century style in the arts based on extravagant design and exuberant decoration

Blank verse unrhymed poetry using iambic pentameters (a special form of rhythm based on short and long syllables)

Chamber music classical music not intended for a full orchestra or soloists, e.g. string quartet

Expressionism a style of art, music, etc. that subordinates realism to expressing the artist's inner feelings

Impressionism a style of art, music, etc. intended to convey the general effect, rather than elaborate detail

Lieder song form of the Romantic era, especially associated with Schubert

Oratorio a work for singers and orchestra (usually with religious connections) to be performed as a concert, rather than an opera

Pas de deux dance in ballet for two persons (usually the male and female leads)

Quality drama plays or films that have most of the criteria for aesthetic evaluation

Romanticism a movement in the arts that emphasised the theme and feelings of a work of art, rather than its form (e.g. Beethoven in music, Wordsworth in literature, Turner in painting)

Sonnet poem of fourteen lines with ten syllables to a line

Stream of consciousness a form of novel writing depicting a continuous flow of a person's thoughts and reactions to events rather than telling a story

Surrealism a movement in art and literature expressing the subconscious through dreams

Aesthetics is the study of what makes something beautiful, what makes something valued as a work of art. In a sense, aesthetic evaluation is a matter of taste. We say someone has good taste or bad taste in areas such as choice of furniture, interior design, clothes, hairstyle, garden ornaments, etc. In the same way, people have good taste or bad taste in culture and the arts. However, there is more to aesthetic evaluation than taste alone. There is a connection between aesthetic values and moral values. Someone can have terrific style and taste in all the other areas previously mentioned and be thoroughly evil without it affecting their taste. However, a work of art that is evil cannot be regarded as a great work of art. Works of art are not just concerned with beauty; they are concerned with human behaviour, the nature and meaning of life, the concepts of good and evil.

Some critics have challenged this view and claim that aesthetic evaluation is solely concerned with the form of a work of art and the effect it has on the person experiencing it. They suggest that it is impossible to know what the artist had in mind when creating the work of art, so all that matters is its effects on the person experiencing it. Some critics, such as Cleanth Brooks, have gone as far as to say that nothing can be said about a work of art; it can only be experienced.

Although it is true that great works of art from the past still function for us as a great work of art, even though we have no idea of their creators' reasons for creating them (e.g. pre-historic cave paintings, Greek sculptures), such a view seems to ignore many factors. If works of art can only be experienced, what is the point of their existence? There can be no greater value in Beethoven than in Sir Cliff Richard. Great art can shock, challenge, even change the lives of those who experience it. People have lost their faith in God through reading books such as Dostoevsky's *The Brothers Karamazov*. People's attitudes to the Spanish Civil War were changed by Picasso's painting, *Guernica*, which was based on an incident in the war. Dictators such as Hitler and Stalin tried to keep firm control of the arts because they saw them as dangerous in provoking criticism and questioning of the regime. The Nazis burnt books whose ideas they disagreed with and censored any art form to make sure that it was promoting the ideals of the regime. All of which indicates that there is something about the arts that can be evaluated. It is possible to draw up a set of criteria to be used when trying to determine whether something is a great work of art and whether one piece of art is better than another (see Figure 18.1).

Using aesthetic evaluation

The criteria for aesthetic evaluation can be used in a wide range of situations. In deciding whether classical music is more beautiful or worthwhile than popular music, it would be possible to show that, in terms of form, classical music is better because of the greater skill required to compose it. However, there may be much more difficulty in determining whether the classical music of Salieri (a contemporary of Mozart, who was equally popular in his day) is more worthwhile than the popular music of the Beatles. The Beatles were far more innovative, their music had more to say about life, and their music is likely to have far more longevity than that of Salieri.

Figure 18.1 Elements within aesthetic evaluation

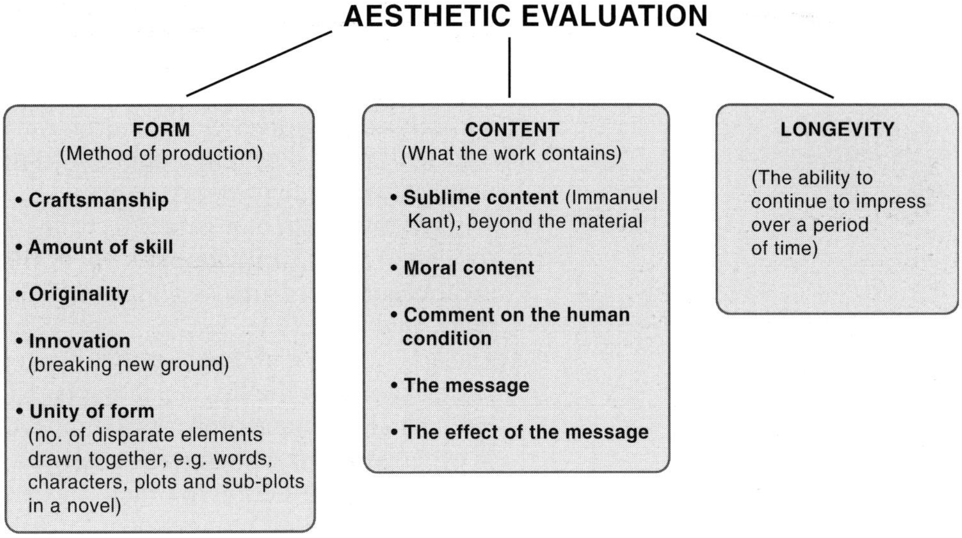

AESTHETIC EVALUATION

FORM
(Method of production)

- **Craftsmanship**

- **Amount of skill**

- **Originality**

- **Innovation**
  (breaking new ground)

- **Unity of form**
  (no. of disparate elements drawn together, e.g. words, characters, plots and sub-plots in a novel)

CONTENT
(What the work contains)

- **Sublime content** (Immanuel Kant), beyond the material

- **Moral content**

- **Comment on the human condition**

- **The message**

- **The effect of the message**

LONGEVITY

(The ability to continue to impress over a period of time)

The criteria can also be used for judging one piece of art against a similar one, for deciding whether a live play is better than a film, a painting by David Hockney is better than a painting by Rembrandt, or a song by one pop star is better than one by another.

However, you should always have a good knowledge of anything to which you apply these criteria. You should also bear in mind the difficulty of drawing a boundary between **popular culture** (widely available, sometimes less educated forms of the arts, such as pop music, popular literature such as thrillers, etc., popular contemporary shows and films) and **high culture** (the arts, such as classical music, opera, ballet, great literature, serious theatre and film).

Government sponsorship of the arts

Arts such as opera, classical music, ballet, serious theatre and even serious film would not survive without government funding. The Arts Council of Great Britain receives government grants to support the arts. In 1992, museums and art galleries received £259 million, libraries received £172 million, films £22 million and other arts £490 million. By 1998, these had been reduced to museums and art galleries £253 million, libraries £127 million, films £23 million and other arts £472 million. At the same time, the cost of administering these grants rose from £16 million in 1992 to £23 million in 1998. However, the fall in government subsidy has been more than offset by the large sums given to the arts by the National Lottery.

The arguments for government sponsorship of the arts

- High culture is a vital part of a nation's culture. Popular culture can survive without subsidy precisely because it can command large audiences, but high culture is expensive to maintain and cannot be financed by the smaller numbers who attend performances.
- The arts are a sign of a society's civilisation. They give the members of the society an opportunity to think about the meaning of life and to experience great beauty. Arts such as sculpture and architecture make the environment more pleasant.
- The arts can make money for the country. Although the domestic performances of the Royal Shakespeare Company require subsidies, their tours abroad make a profit. More importantly, many tourists come to Britain to experience our wide range of cultural activities. Their money makes a substantial contribution to Britain's exports (money spent by tourists in Britain is an export; money spent by British tourists abroad is an import).
- The popular arts such as music and theatre depend on the training given by high culture. Many of the production teams and backing groups for pop stars have a classical music training. Actors in popular theatre and television have often had a classical training.
- As seen in Issue 19 ('The nature of culture'), there is no clear division between high culture and popular culture and it could be that a society without high culture would also lose much of its popular culture.
- Market forces can lead to a serious downgrading of culture. The argument about the BBC being funded by licence rather than advertising (a form of subsidy because there are people who buy a licence but never watch the BBC's programmes) is usually based on a comparison between BBC

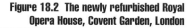

Figure 18.2 The newly refurbished Royal Opera House, Covent Garden, London

No trainers or jeans

The new Royal Opera House in Covent Garden London cost £214 million to build. As the Royal Opera could not raise the money, the National Lottery gave £78 million. The Government is also giving the Opera House £20 million a year through the Arts Council for running costs (4.2% of all Arts Council spending). However, only 20% of tickets are available to the public, the rest go to sponsors of the Opera House in order of how much they have given.

① Re-read the novel you did for GCSE English and use the aesthetic evaluation criteria to explain why it is/is not a great work of art.

② Choose an area of popular music you enjoy and explain why you enjoy it.

③ Choose a painting, piece of classical music, play or film that is considered to be a great work of art and use all the information in this issue to discuss whether it really is a great work of art (argue the points for and the points against).

④ 'Only the rich enjoy the arts so the arts should not be subsidised by government taxes.' Examine the validity of this statement. (This means just the same as discuss!)

programmes and those on the satellite and cable channels, which are solely determined by market forces. If quality television requires subsidy, then quality arts should also receive subsidy.

- All governments now subsidise the arts, so that if Britain stopped doing so, all the best artists would go overseas.

The arguments against government sponsorship of the arts

- The people who want high culture and who go to the opera, etc. are the relatively well off, who are able to pay the market price for their seats (a French survey of the arts showed that less than 10% of audiences at serious theatre, opera and symphony concerts were working class).
- Most government subsidy is spent on the arts in London, which is unfair to people in the regions.
- In every other area of life workers are paid the market rate and if their industry cannot compete it has to reduce wages and costs. The same economics should apply to serious theatre, opera, etc., wages and costs should be reduced until subsidies are not needed.
- Writers of serious literature survive without subsidy and many serious films make profits.
- The people who decide on arts sponsorship are people from within the arts industry. Subsidies should be organised by ordinary people and the arts industries wanting the subsidy should have to justify their claims for subsidy.
- There are much more important things to spend hundreds of millions of pounds on than the arts – such as the homeless, world poverty or the National Health Service.

Specimen exam questions

AS 'I know what I like, and that's all there is to it.' Why is such a response to a work of art probably inadequate? What criteria should be used in judging a work of art?

A2 'The arts are only entertainment, and, although enjoyable, they are of no use to society.' Discuss this view with reference to more than one art form.

19

The nature of culture

Culture can be defined in a variety of ways, but it is generally agreed that culture means human beliefs, knowledge and behaviour, which form a distinctive pattern or system. Each society has its own culture based on such things as a separate language, a separate history, different rituals and customs (e.g. French culture, Scottish culture, Maori culture). This idea of culture has led to stereotyping, so that Scottish culture is often seen in terms of associations such as the kilt, the bagpipes, haggis, Burns' Night and tossing the caber.

However, in the second half of the twentieth century, cultures began to mix much more and the old monocultural idea (where each society has only one culture, which everyone accepts and lives by) has been displaced, as most societies have become multicultural. In a multicultural society, there may be groups living according to a variety of ethnic cultures, but there will also be some subcultures such as teen culture, urban culture, rural culture, pop culture, mass culture, high culture. Sociologists now accept that the culture into which an individual is born may have a much smaller influence than it used to have. Individuals now have the opportunity to choose their own culture, in the sense that in a multicultural society any individual will be influenced by several cultures.

In order to help you to answer questions on culture, this issue will explain some of the more common types of culture.

Western culture

Western culture is the basic culture of Europe and the USA and has a major effect on most other cultures in the world. Much argument about culture is based around whether it is inevitable that all cultures will eventually become subcultures of western culture and whether western culture has a good or bad effect. Japan is a typical example of this argument. Its economy and media are thoroughly western culture, but Japanese culture still dominates many people's personal lives (attitudes towards and rituals concerning birth, marriage death, festivals, etc.).

The main features of western culture are:

- a concern for individual rights – free speech, freedom to choose or reject religion, free choice of marriage partner, freedom for an individual to move from the bottom to the top of society, freedom from arbitrary arrest (if arrested, people must be brought before an open court within a short length of time);
- equality of opportunity – free education available to everyone, all jobs (especially government jobs) open to anyone, legislation against racist or sexist bias;
- protection of the poor – healthcare and payments to the unemployed, the sick and the old through taxation;
- democratic systems of government;
- the arts following certain forms (see 'High culture' and 'Popular culture' below);
- dress and lifestyle based on the individual, rather the group;
- festivals and holidays based on Christianity (e.g. Christmas and Easter);

- moral values based on Christianity (respect for monogamy, honesty, loving one's neighbour, etc.);
- the media reflecting the lifestyles and arts (especially popular culture) and having great importance in people's lives.

Many people would not accept all these features and some critics of western culture see its key features and symbols as jeans, Coca Cola, McDonalds and pop music, which they also see as destroying the indigenous cultures of the world.

High culture

KEY words

American dream the alleged basis of American culture, that any individual can do anything they want and achieve the lifestyle they desire through using market forces

Booker Prize the most important British literature award for newly written serious novels

Ethnic originally connected with race, it is now used to refer more to a cultural group, which may have certain racial characteristics (e.g. gypsies, Sikhs)

Grand opera opera in which there is no spoken dialogue; everything is set to music

Indigenous culture the culture that is native to the area (e.g. the culture of the native Americans is the indigenous culture of the USA)

Monoculture a society whose life is based on only one culture

Multiculture a society with several different cultures

Multiethnic a society with different races and cultures connected with those races

Pop art serious art based on popular culture and the mass media, e.g. Andy Warhol's painting of a can of Campbell's soup

Turner Prize the most important British award for contemporary art (painting and sculpture)

Whitbread Prize a British award for the best book of the year

Many people link culture with the arts and use the term 'cultured person' to refer to someone who appreciates, and is knowledgeable about, classical music, opera, ballet, great literature, poetry, serious theatre and film, painting and sculpture. It is claimed that this type of culture is a sign of civilisation because these arts speak to us about the meaning of life, speak to 'the human spirit' and pass on human values.

Classical music

This includes music written either for a symphony orchestra or for groups of instruments from the orchestra. A symphony orchestra is made up of strings (violins, violas, cellos, double bass), woodwind (clarinets, oboes, bassoons, flutes, cor anglais, piccolos), brass (horns, trumpets, trombones and tubas) and percussion (drums, cymbals, etc.). The main types of music played by a symphony orchestra are symphonies, concertos (solo instrument and orchestra) and overtures. However, symphony orchestras can also be used to accompany choirs in major choral works such as Handel's *Messiah*, Bach's *St Matthew Passion* and the great masses such as the *Requiems* of Mozart and Fauré. The first great concertos were written by J. S. Bach (*Brandenburg Concertos*) and Vivaldi (*The Four Seasons*); the first great symphonies were written by Haydn (*London Symphonies*), Mozart (*Jupiter Symphony*) and Beethoven (*Eroica Symphony*). Classical music did not end with Beethoven. Mendelssohn, Lizst, Brahms, Mahler, Stravinsky, Rachmaninov, Elgar and Britten continued and evolved the tradition. There are many composers still writing classical music, such as John Taverner, whose *Requiem* was played at the funeral of Princess Diana.

Opera

This can be defined as 'drama set to music where the music is essential to the drama'. The first operas were performed in Italy (e.g. Monteverdi's *Coronation of Poppea*) and developed by Gluck (e.g. *Orpheus*) and Mozart (e.g. *Don Giovanni, The Marriage of Figaro, The Magic Flute*). Opera depends on the plot as well as the music, solo singers who act the main parts, often a chorus of singers and a symphony orchestra (though this is often smaller than a full orchestra). Many people see opera as the highest form of culture because it combines classical music with theatre and art in the sets and costumes. This also makes opera the most expensive art form to perform. The most popular operas today are those by Mozart, Verdi (e.g. *Nabucco*, *Aida*, *Il Traviata*), Wagner (e.g. *Die Meistersingers*, *The Ring*), Bizet (e.g. *Carmen*, *The Pearl Fishers*), and Puccini (e.g. *La Boheme*, *Madame Butterfly*, *Tosca*). Opera singers such as Caruso, Maria Callas and Luciano Pavarotti can achieve as much fame and money as great pop stars.

Ballet

This is a form of dancing to classical music that has been popular in all cultures from earliest times. Ballet began in France in the late seventeenth century, with the work of the French composer Lully. Much of modern ballet developed in the nineteenth century in France, but some of the great changes to modern ballet occurred in Russia, under Diagilev, just before the communist revolution. Famous female ballet dancers include Isadora Duncan, Maria Pavlova and Margot Fonteyn. The two most famous male ballet dancers were both Russian: Vaclav Nijinsky and Rudolph Nureyev. The most popular ballets today are probably those of Tchaikovsky (*The Nutcracker*, *Swan Lake*, *Romeo and Juliet*), Delibes (*Coppelia*) and Stravinsky (*Petroushka*, *The Rite of Spring*, *The Firebird*). The ballet requires a symphony orchestra and so is often staged in opera houses. In England the Royal Ballet and the Royal Opera both use the New Covent Garden Opera House.

Great literature

This refers to novels or short stories that have a message about the meaning of life and say something about human nature through their characters (though their storyline may or may not stand up to scrutiny). The novel you studied for GCSE English literature will be termed as 'great literature'. The first great piece of English literature can probably be regarded as *The Canterbury Tales* by Chaucer. Novels did not evolve until the eighteenth century, when *Joseph Andrewes* by Henry Fielding and *Robinson Crusoe* by Daniel Defoe were written. The greatest nineteenth-century British novelist was Charles Dickens (*David Copperfield*, *Great Expectations*, *Oliver Twist*), though some would claim that it was Jane Austen (*Pride and Prejudice*, *Sense and Sensibility*) or the Brontë sisters (*Jane Eyre*, *Wuthering Heights*). Twentieth-century novelists such as D. H. Lawrence (*Sons and Lovers*, *Women in Love*), James Joyce (*Ulysses*), John Braine (*Room at the Top*) have tended to be more working class than in previous centuries. There are many contemporary novelists writing what may be considered 'great literature' such as William Trevor, Salman Rushdie (*Midnight's Children*, *Satanic Verses*), Martin Amis and Margaret Forster. You should be aware of great world literature such as *War and Peace* by Leo Tolstoy (about Russian aristocratic families during and after the Napoleonic Wars), *The Brothers Karamazov* by Fyodor Dostoevsky (about murder and the existence of God) and *A La Recherche du Temps Perdu* by Marcel Proust (about the decline of a group of French aristocrats at the beginning of the twentieth century).

Poetry

It is often said that 'a poem can say in a page what it takes a novel 300 pages to say'. It is also said that poetry is 'the best words in the best order'. From this it can be seen that poetry is about putting forward ideas about the meaning of life, and also about using words in special ways to give a beautiful sound, as well as a deep meaning. There is a close connection between poetry and other

Did you know?

'Have a bon jour'

The French government is worried that French culture is being taken over by American culture. The *Academie Française* (which is in charge of the French language) has written French words for the many English words that have come into the average French vocabulary (e.g. le jogging, le weekend, le pop music, le duty-free – such words are called Franglais). The *Academie* is trying to persuade French people to use the French words. In the same way, French chefs are complaining about the effects of McDonalds fast food on French restaurants and are running campaigns to persuade French people to eat French food. There are also attempts to ban British and American films and pop music in order to protect and encourage French culture. However, it appears that ordinary French people are not responding to these attempts to save French culture.

forms of literature. Shakespeare wrote poems as well as plays (they are called sonnets because of the verse form). Thomas Hardy, who wrote great novels such as *Tess of the d'Urbervilles* and *Jude the Obscure*, also wrote much poetry. One of the great periods in English poetry was the Romantic period of the early nineteenth century, whose writers included Wordsworth (*Daffodils, Upon Westminster Bridge*), Keats (*Ode to a Nightingale, Endymion*), Shelley (*Ozymandias, To a Skylark*) and Coleridge (*Kubla Khan, The Rime of the Ancient Mariner*). You will probably have studied twentieth-century poetry for GCSE English; try re-reading some of it to see whether your views about it have changed.

Serious theatre and film

This is difficult to define. However, it would probably be argued that a serious film or play is saying something about life, rather than just trying to entertain. It will be well written and very well acted by actors who are known for their ability to play serious roles. In the theatre, Shakespeare is clearly 'serious theatre', but just as Shakespeare wrote comedies and tragedies, so playwrights such as Alan Ayckbourn (*Comic Potential*) or Michael Frayn (*Copenhagen*) are seen as serious, even though they are writing comedies. However, a play such as *The Mousetrap* by Agathie Christie, which has been running in the West End continuously for 48 years, is not seen as serious theatre. In the same way, films such as *Dogma*, *East is East* and *Hold Back the Night* would be seen as serious films because of their attempts to deal with the meaning of life, whereas films such as *End of Days* or *American Pie* would not.

Painting and sculpture

These have been part of human life from prehistoric times. Some of the earliest examples of human culture are cave paintings, the most famous being those from Northern Spain and South West France, dating from over 40 000 years ago. The Egyptian civilisation is remembered both by its sculpture, such as the huge statues of pharaohs, and by the intricate paintings on the walls of the tombs and on the sarcophagi (coffins of the mummies). Of course, painting and sculpture is joined together in architecture, which often reflects the spirit of an age. The most famous ancient sculptures come from Greece (e.g. *Venus de Milo*), where sculptures began to be made from bronze as well as marble. In Western Europe most art took the form of architecture until the Renaissance, when painting and sculpture enjoyed a rebirth. Michelangelo is famous not only for the paintings on the ceiling of the Sistine Chapel (frescoes depicting Christianity from Adam to the final judgement), but also great sculptures such as *David* and *Pieta*. After the Renaissance, there have been several different periods and styles: Baroque (Bernini, El Greco, Carravaggio, Rembrandt), Rococo (Canaletto, Watteau), Romantic (Goya, Turner), Impressionist (Renoir, Degas, Monet, Cezanne), Expressionist (Van Gogh, Roualt, Munch and abstract expressionist in Jackson Pollock), Surrealist (Klee, Magritte, Dali). The most famous sculptors of these periods have been Bernini, Rodin and Henry Moore.

Figure 19.1 The Angel of the North, created by a high culture sculptor, but most admired by ordinary people who follow popular culture

Popular culture

Popular culture is often used in a derogatory sense to indicate the type of culture that is less educated and less valuable than high culture. However, each area of high culture has a corresponding feature in popular culture. Music is perhaps the easiest example, where popular music is a major business worldwide. Groups and popstars can attract massive audiences at concerts almost anywhere in the world and their records sell millions of copies. Closely connected with popular music is a variety of dance forms from ordinary people dancing in a nightclub to professional dancers in modern dance shows. Popular literature ranges from thrillers and romances to biographies of sports and pop stars. Theatres and cinemas make their money from the popular shows and films they put on. Andy Warhol developed a form of painting that he called pop art, but no painting can ever be popular in one sense because only the rich can afford to buy original paintings. However, most homes will have some cheap reproductions of famous paintings, which may reveal that paintings are often more a part of popular culture than high culture, e.g. Constable's *Haywain*. Many modern sculptures are publicly funded and can become popular because they are in places frequented by the public. *The Angel of the North* in Gateshead seems to be more popular with ordinary people than with those who consider themselves 'cultured', and as such is perhaps an example of popular sculpture.

This sculpture also identifies a major problem with trying to make a division between high culture and popular culture, as there are so many fringe areas. James Horner's theme music for *Titanic* appeared in both the pop music charts and the classical music charts. Serious films such as *Brassed Off* and *The Full Monty* have also been hugely popular. Perhaps this is more easily seen in television, where traditionally Channel 3 is the popular culture channel with BBC2 and Channel 4 as the high culture channels, although it is Channel 3 that screens *The South Bank Show*, a programme all about high culture. The differences between high and popular culture (and the fact that high culture can only survive through subsidies from the taxes of people who do not like it) are all dealt with at greater length in Issue 18 ('Aesthetic evaluation').

Specimen exam questions

AS Assess the claim that high culture is superior to and therefore more important than popular culture.

A2 It has been said that the major development in the arts in the twentieth century is that they have become more accessible to ordinary people and therefore more widely enjoyed than ever before. Discuss to what extent this can be said to be true, using specific illustrations drawn from any branch of the arts.

CTIVITIES

① Interview people of a variety of ages and social situations to discover what they consider to be the key features of British culture.

② Use the Internet to discover the main features of popular culture.

③ Listen to 30 minutes of Classic FM, 30 minutes of Radio 1 and 30 minutes of an Asian radio programme. Decide whether the music played on Classic FM or the Asian station has most in common with the music of Radio 1 and why.

④ Make a list of the arguments for and against western culture being adopted throughout the world.

20

Censorship

Forms of censorship

When westerners think of censorship, they tend to think of the type of censorship that once existed in the Soviet Union and still exists, to a certain extent, in countries such as the People's Republic of China. Under such governments, the media are owned by the government and only publish the views of the government. Plays and books have to be submitted to a government censor prior to publication.

The justification for such a form of censorship is to protect the state from being weakened, either by hostile powers being given access to its secrets, or by its institutions being weakened by criticism. If you believe that your form of government and its institutions are the best (as most communist or totalitarian governments do), then you will believe that they should not be weakened in any way. Such governments also feel that the people who live in their society should be protected from the misinformation that capitalist societies try to feed to them in order to bring them back under the control of capitalism. Non-communist governments opposed to freedom of information and so imposing media censorship may do so because they think their people should be protected from lies. A fundamentalist Muslim government may feel that anything not based on the *Qur'an* is untrue and that the citizens should be protected from it.

The United States Constitution states that there should be a right to freedom of speech and freedom of the press. This is why all societies with democratic forms of government (as in western society) claim to believe in freedom of expression. In order for democracy to work, the electorate has to be able to make informed choices before they vote. For this, they need a free press so that they can know what is going on in the world and in their own country and can work out which political party will deal best with the problems of the country and the world.

Even so, most democracies have forms of censorship in certain areas.

Censorship and the press

In some countries, especially France, there are privacy laws preventing the press from publishing any stories that infringe upon an individual's right to privacy. It is sometimes claimed that this law is the reason why French politicians are not as worried by the press as British politicians. In Britain there are three forms of press censorship.

- *D-notices.* The government can issue the press with a D-notice under the Official Secrets Act to prevent them from publishing anything classed as an official secret. There have been a few occasions when a newspaper has ignored a D-notice in the public interest, for example when a civil servant has leaked a piece of information showing the government to be breaking the law.

- *Obscene Publications Act* . Under this act, a newspaper or publisher can be charged with a criminal offence if they publish something that is obscene. The definition of obscene varies, from the 1868 British definition – 'whatever has a tendency to deprave and corrupt those whose minds are open to such immoral influences' – to the 1973 American definition – 'works which portray sexual conduct in a patently offensive way, and which, taken as a whole, do not have serious literary, artistic, political or scientific value'.
- *Defamation of character* (libel when written, slander when spoken). If the press publishes an article defaming someone's character, and is untrue, then they can be sued for damages. The damages can be enormous (Jeffrey Archer received £3 million from the *Daily Star* when they accused him of having sex with a prostitute and could not prove it).

Blasphemy speech or action manifesting contempt for God

Index a list, which used to be compiled by the Roman Catholic Church until 1966, of books that Catholics were not allowed to read

Libel defaming a person in writing

Official Secrets Act makes it an offence for anyone who has ever served the Crown (civil servants, armed forces, etc.) to communicate any information acquired in that service, whether harmful to the state or not

Pornography the representation of erotic behaviour in books, pictures, films, etc. that is intended to arouse sexual excitement

Pre-publication censorship the censorship imposed before people have a chance to see it, e.g. film censorship, D-notices

Post-publication censorship censorship imposed after people have seen it, e.g. libel and slander laws

Quis custodet ipsos custodes? literally, 'Who guards the guardians?'. It comes from Plato's Republic, where Plato suggested that a perfect society would have a group of guardians who would protect the people from harmful ideas

Slander defaming a person in speech – there is a legal argument as to whether defamation on radio or television is libel or slander

Censorship and television

Television is covered by all the same censorship regulations as the press, but has some additional regulations.

The 'watershed' is a voluntary code of practice under which the television companies agree only to screen programmes of 'a family nature' before 9.00 p.m. This is self-censorship, aimed at the protection of children.

In addition, there are extra requirements for the self-censorship of ITV. The Broadcasting Act requires the Independent Television Committee (ITC) to ensure that nothing is included in programmes that 'offends against good taste or decency'. The ITC's own code of conduct requires that there should be no abusive treatment of religious views or beliefs and no 'improper exploitation of any susceptibilities of those watching programmes'. Furthermore, the ITC requires that any adverts shown on television must be 'legal, decent, honest and truthful' and that companies sponsoring programmes must be suitable for the subject content of the programme.

The BBC is controlled by its charter, which requires it to produce a range of programmes that uphold the standards of public decency. After the 1990 Broadcasting Act, which established the ITC, the BBC set up its own Programme Complaints Unit, to which the public can complain if they think programmes have offended standards of decency or have been biased. The BBC has also published a set of *Producers' Guidelines* showing how producers are prevented from producing programmes which give an unbalanced view of a political issue or offend public decency.

Censorship and the arts

The Lord Chamberlain's Office used to view all theatre productions and censor them for obscenity, until it was ended by the Labour government of 1966–70. Today, the theatre is only censored by the same obscenity and defamation laws

Did you know?

Have you heard this one?

- 'Blue jokes', meaning jokes with sexual innuendo, originate from the days of theatre censorship, when the Lord Chamberlain's Office would put a blue line through scripts or jokes with sexual innuendo.

- Sir Karl Popper, one of the greatest twentieth-century philosophers, argued that freedom of expression is essential in order for human societies to make progress. He claimed that it is no accident that the most advanced societies also have the greatest freedom for their citizens. According to Popper, progress is made by subjecting all ideas, policies, etc. to scrutiny, discovering what is false in them and then putting forward a new form without the false elements. This can only happen if, for example, government policies can be investigated by a free press, opposition parties, trades unions, employers, etc.

as the press and television. However, many theatres operate a voluntary policy of indicating to the public if a performance may cause offence or is unsuitable for children.

All films must be submitted to the British Board of Film Classification for a viewing category. The categories must be enforced by cinema owners who can be prosecuted if under-age children are watching '12', '15' or '18' films. The Board can also cut scenes from films if it considers that they are too graphic in their portrayal of sex or violence. It is also possible for the Board to refuse to grant a certificate to a film, and local councils can refuse permission for such films to be shown in their area. The Board used to justify its work in terms of 'preserving public decency', but now it justifies it in terms of the guidance its categories give to parents and cinema owners.

In a question on censorship in the arts, the information on television could also be used.

The case for censorship

The amount of censorship currently existing in the UK is usually justified by some or all of the following arguments:

- Children have a right to be protected from adult material. There is evidence of children being influenced by what they see because they are too young and inexperienced to have worked out their own ideas and opinions on adult issues. (You could quote the Jamie Bulger case or the Helen Mirren film *Killing Mrs Tingle*, which was banned in Germany after children plotted to kill their teachers when they received low grades, like the children in the film.)
- People have a right not to have their sensibilities offended. So, old people have a right not to be confronted by graphic sex scenes, obscene language, etc. on their televisions; members of religions have a right not to see their beliefs ridiculed, etc. People who argue for censorship in this way claim that there is a difference between 'free-to-air' television, radio and the Internet, where people have no control over what is on and 'pay-to-view' television and the theatre, where subscribers only see what they have paid to see. They argue that there is much less need for censorship when there is no free access.
- Film and television directors, newspaper publishers, etc. are motivated by greed and profit and should not be able to make money by gratifying people's baser desires.
- The press needs to be prevented from intruding on people's privacy. Famous people should have a right to a private life and the *paparazzi* should be banned from taking photographs without permission. In the same way, people should have a right to freedom from press intrusion in moments of family crisis, such as after a murder or a plane crash.

ACTIVITIES

① Read some tabloid newspapers to find a scandal story about a famous person. Investigate the story and work out which public interests were served by publishing the story and what the effects of not publishing the story might have been.

② Make a list of the problems parents might encounter in trying to ensure that a child does not see or read anything offensive until they are 15.

③ Discuss the problems the Internet poses for censorship, e.g. scandal, obscene publications, private activities of famous/powerful people, mis-information.

④ Use the Internet to discover freedom of information laws in the USA and the UK. Make a list of the differences and explain which system you would prefer.

⑤ Blasphemy against the Christian religion is still a criminal offence. It is rarely used and some members of ethnic communities have suggested that it should be extended to make it an offence to denigrate any religion. What problems can you see in trying to impose such a law in a multifaith community?

⑥ Interview people from varying age groups to see what they would regard as a programme which 'offended public decency'.

The case against censorship

Those who argue against censorship are often in favour of a system such as film categories in order to protect children and people's sensibilities. They also accept the need for defamation laws to protect people from untrue things being published about them. However, they would oppose all other forms of censorship, including the Official Secrets Act. They hold the following views:

• Any democracy needs freedom of information. How can voters make informed decisions in elections and referenda if facts are kept from them?
• Who decides what needs to be kept secret or what needs to be censored, and, perhaps even more importantly, who is there to check that their decision is correct?
• If obscenity and violence are corrupting, then the censors, who spend their lives watching such things to decide that other people cannot see them ought to be very corrupt.
• Censorship has always been impossible to impose completely. The rich and powerful have always been able to gain access to what was denied to the mass of the population. Nowadays, with new technology and the advent of the Internet, effective censorship is impossible.
• Privacy laws can be, and have been, used by the powerful to cover up their misdeeds. Who is to decide whether a politician having an affair is in the public interest, other than the press?

Specimen exam questions

AS State what you believe to be the arguments, (a) for censorship; and (b) against censorship in the arts.

A2 Explain, with the use of examples and illustrations, why the question of censorship is such a difficult and complex issue to resolve in a modern, democratic society.

Creativity and innovation

Makes you think

Creativity and innovation is a vital part of science, maths and philosophy, as well the arts. Rene Descartes (1596–1650) is known as the father of modern philosophy. When he read about the ideas of Copernicus and Galileo, he realised that all he had been taught at school about science was wrong. This also led him to realise that he had accepted what other people told him without trying to find out for himself whether it was true, so that everything he had learned might be false. This led Descartes to develop what has become known as 'systematic doubt'. This means doubting everything until you come to what cannot be doubted. In the process of doubting everything, Descartes realised that he could not doubt his own existence because there must be something to be doing the doubting. From this came Descartes' famous statement, 'Cogito ergo sum' ('I think therefore I am'). The creativity and innovation of Descartes led to later philosophical and scientific ideas about truth, the importance of maths for science and the scientific method.

Creativity can have many meanings. There is a sense in which everyone is creative. Anyone who has written a letter, decorated a room or planted out a garden has been creative. However, calling someone creative is usually taken to mean more than this; it is used to refer to people who write books, paint pictures or create designer gardens.

Innovation is more clearcut. To count as an innovation, what is created must be different from what has gone before. It must break new ground, by starting a new school of art, as the Impressionists Renoir and Degas did, developing the form of the symphony as Beethoven did, or, like the Beatles, changing the direction of popular music.

Creativity and ordinary people

Many experts believe that all human beings have a creative urge and so they believe that education should give people the opportunity to develop that creativity. The purpose of art, music, cookery, woodwork, metalwork, needlework, drama, design lessons at school is to encourage creativity, and also to give young people the opportunity to discover whether they have particular creative gifts and to give them the skills to use their gifts. It is often argued that many great artists will never be able to reveal their creative gifts if they are not given skills and opportunities in creative subjects. In just the same way that Shakespeare could not have written his plays if he had not been taught to read and write; likewise no one can become a great violinist if they never have the chance to learn to play a violin or become a great designer if they are not given the necessary basic skills. This is seen very clearly in Sir Paul McCartney, who composed all the music for his classical piece *Standing Stones*, but had to have expert help to write it into an orchestral score because he had never actually been taught musical composition.

It is also argued that those who take part in the arts, in even the most basic way, are more able to appreciate them than those who only go to watch. Someone who has played in a school orchestra knows how hard it is to get a group of musicians to play correctly. They also have some understanding of musical forms, and so are more able to appreciate great music. Someone who has tried to paint or sculpt is likely to have far more appreciation of a painting or sculpture than someone who has not, because they are aware of the technical problems involved. Likewise, people who have sung in choirs or acted in school plays are likely to have a better appreciation of choral music or theatre than someone who has not.

However, it can also be argued that anyone who has creative urges and skills will be driven to use them. Sir Paul McCartney may not have written and performed the great pop music he has if he had been trained in music. It can be argued that if he had been trained, he would not have had the originality or the desire to perform that a great pop musician needs. He has been a great musician without training. In the same way, artists like van Gogh and Gauguin had no formal art training, but felt a compelling urge to paint. Very few novelists have any formal training in literature.

In the same way, it is possible that music lessons and art lessons put many young people off the arts in the same way that teaching Shakespeare, rather than going to see performances of his plays, puts young people off Shakespeare for life.

Le Corbusier and modern architecture

Charles Jeanneret (1887–1965), who adopted the pseudonym Le Corbusier (the name of one of his ancestors) when he started writing, was the most famous of a group of artists and architects who wanted to break away from traditional forms. In *Towards a New Architecture*, Le Corbusier put forward the view that architecture should be functional, rather than decorated – 'A house is a machine for living in', 'a curved street is a donkey track, a straight street, a road for men'. Le Corbusier utilised the new invention of reinforced concrete to build a shell of concrete floors resting on steel girders so that the outside of his buildings could be of any material – he most often used glass – that would keep plain vertical and horizontal lines. He also believed that the city of the future would be full of green areas and parks with all the living spaces and offices being in skyscrapers.

Le Corbusier found it difficult to get his designs built (a workers' city he built in Pessac, France, in 1926 was so hated by the local authority that it refused to pipe water to it), but his books illustrated with his designs had a tremendous impact on young and trainee architects. By 1950, his ideas had become so influential that he was able to design a complex of housing and shops for 1800 people in Marseilles. In 1951, he was made architectural adviser for the construction of Chandigarh, the brand new capital of the Punjab Province of India. His use of unfinished concrete for the principal buildings of the city had an immediate impact on architecture around the world. What is often called 'modern architecture' high rise, straight line, functional buildings using concrete and glass is the result of Le Corbusier's successful fight against the conservative forces of architecture (see Figure 21.1).

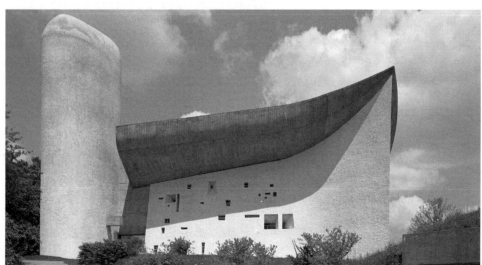

Figure 21.1 A building by Le Corbusier

Monet and Impressionism

Claude Monet (1840–1926) was the son of a successful grocer and ship's chandler in Le Havre. He began painting in his mid-teens, and, though he went to Paris, he refused the formal art training his father wanted to pay for, preferring to work with artists. Throughout his life Monet was fascinated by the *effects of light* on how objects are perceived. Oil painted landscapes were painted in studios after remembrances or sketches of the real thing. Monet insisted on painting his landscapes outdoors so that the perception could be put onto canvas immediately.

In 1869 Monet went to La Grenouillère, a resort on the Seine, to paint with Renoir. Together they painted what were to be regarded as the first Impressionist paintings, recording on the spot the impression of a scene rather than a detailed study. This was done by interpreting the light and movement by *rapid, short strokes and fairly vivid colours*. It was Monet's painting, *Impression: Sunrise*, shown at an exhibition in Paris in 1874, which led the critics to call this school of painting 'Impressionism'. Other famous painters worked in the same style and exhibited with Monet and Renoir (e.g. Degas, Pissarro, Cezanne). However, the artists gradually drew apart and began to develop different styles; the last Impressionist exhibition was held in 1886.

Monet himself continued to paint in his impressionistic style through paintings that studied a single subject through varying lights. As he became more famous, he used the money to develop a garden at his new home in Giverny (now a French national monument), which he painted in his later years. Between 1906 and 1926 he painted a series of *Water Lilies*, in which the actual features become more and more indistinct, with just a shimmering series of colours giving the overall impression of sunlight playing on a lily pond.

Monet was not only an innovative creator; his ideas have had an influence on all the modern schools of art. The exhibition of his paintings at London's Royal Academy in 1999 was a sell-out, the most successful art exhibition ever held in London.

Specimen exam questions

AS 'Only those who have participated in the arts can understand the arts.' To what extent do you agree with this statement?

A2 The twentieth century was a time of great change and innovation in the arts. With reference to *one* of the art forms listed below, describe the major artistic changes that have occurred during the past 100 years: art; architecture; classical music; drama; literature; film.

ACTIVITIES

① Think of any creative activity you have ever been involved in (especially to do with music, art or drama – remember what you did at Junior School) and try to analyse its good and bad effects on you.

② Find examples of the work of either Le Corbusier or Monet and use the criteria from Issue 17 ('Aesthetic evaluation') and the knowledge from this issue to assess their greatness.

③ Work out the arguments for and against giving every school child the right to learn a musical instrument.

④ Many works of art (novels, films, plays, paintings, etc.) are created as vehicles for political, social and/or moral comment. Choose any one work of art that has influenced your thinking about life and society, and explain its purposes and impact on you.

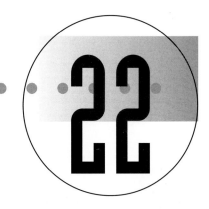

The media

The word 'media' relates to any form of communication between a small group and a larger group. It is usually thought of in terms of the mass media i.e. communication with a mass audience. The most important forms of mass media are: the press (newspapers), radio and television. However, it is important to remember that cinema, magazines and books are also part of the media. The most important recent addition to mass media is the Internet, which enables individuals anywhere in the world to communicate with a worldwide mass audience (see Issue 9, 'Computers').

Broadsheet the name given in the UK to 'quality' newspapers

Elite a small group that considers itself/is considered superior to the rest of society

Establishment social group exercising control over the rest of society

Hard news newspaper stories about real issues and which would make TV news headlines, compared with soft news, which is more 'magaziney'

Hyper-reality believing that television programmes, especially soaps, are more real than reality

Investigative journalism journalists creating news by investigating illegal or scandalous activities

IRN Independent Radio News, an independent company producing news for independent radio stations

ITN Independent Television News, a similar company for television

ITC Independent Television Commission, the body in charge of Channels 3, 4 and 5

New technology in the media this is used to refer especially to computerised printing so that journalists can type in their stories directly

Paparazzi news photographers and journalists who try to get unexpected photos of famous people

Pulitzer Prize American prize awarded for investigative journalism

Reuters the largest of the news agencies, with journalists worldwide and which sells its stories and photos to newspapers and magazines that cannot afford to fund so many journalists

Tabloid name given to popular newspapers in Britain

The press

In the UK, the press is dominated by the national press. There are regional daily morning newspapers such as the *Northern Echo* and the *Yorkshire Post* and regional evening papers such as the *Manchester Evening News*, but over 90% of the morning newspaper market belongs to the nationals.

The national press is traditionally divided into 'popular' and 'quality'. The popular press aims at a large circulation (85% of sales go to the popular press). The popular press is largely represented by *The Sun, The Daily Mirror, The Daily Star, The Express* and *The Daily Mail*, although the latter two regard themselves as in between popular and quality and are aimed at a more educated and discerning reader than the other three. Sometimes the popular press is called 'the gutter press' because of its tendency to publish sensational stories about the private lives of the rich and famous. These five dailies are also called 'tabloid' because of the size of the paper.

The quality press is represented by *The Times, The Guardian, The Daily Telegraph, The Independent* and *The Financial Times*. These newspapers are aimed at an educated, middle-class market and are often called 'broadsheets' because they have large size pages with much more print than the tabloids. They rely heavily on advertising for their income (as do the tabloids, but not as much).

Newspapers as we know them began in the seventeenth century and the first English newspaper was *The Weekly Newes*, which appeared in 1622. Although gimmicks and sensational reporting are generally thought of as something new, they are not. (In 1890, *The Daily Mail* offered £1 a week for life to any reader who could guess the value of the gold in the Bank of England.) However, all journalists see that the press has an important role to play in informing the public and in ensuring that the government and political parties are subjected to regular scrutiny.

The press is controlled by the Press Complaints Council (run by the press itself), D-notices and the laws of libel (see Issue 20, 'Censorship').

Radio

Radio in the UK is divided into those stations funded by the BBC (through money raised by the television licence) and independent stations funded by advertising. Both BBC and independent radio are also divided into national and local stations. The BBC's national stations are Radio 1 (mainly popular music), Radio 2 (light music and entertainment), Radio 3 (classical music and cultural programmes), Radio 4 (news and spoken word programmes) and Radio 5 (sport and current affairs). The BBC's 30 local radio stations use Radio 2 or 4 when not broadcasting their own programmes.

All radio stations have to be licensed and the independent radio stations are licensed by the Independent Radio Authority. There are three national independent radio stations: Classic FM (broadcasting popular classical music and news), Virgin Radio (broadcasting popular music with some chat shows) and Talk Radio UK (broadcasting phone-ins and chat shows). There are over 50 local independent FM radio stations.

Both BBC and independent radio can have their licences revoked by the government, so it can be claimed they are not completely free (see also Issue 20, 'Censorship').

Television

Television is the most rapidly expanding form of the media. In the UK, the most watched television is still provided by the terrestrial stations (the BBC provides Channels 1 and 2 from the licence fee, independent regionally based stations provide Channel 3 and Channels 4 and 5 are both separate national independent stations). However, the growth of satellite, cable and digital broadcasting has led to many more stations being available and also to links between television and the Internet. The Independent Television Commission (ITC) is responsible for licensing all independent television stations, including cable and satellite. It awards licences to the regional ITV companies on the basis of their past record, their proposed schedules and the amount of revenue they intend to give to the government. The ITC is responsible for the content of the programmes and advertising put out by Channels 3, 4, and 5 and enforces government codes on advertising and violence. The terrestrial independent stations are funded solely from revenue from advertising during 'natural breaks', whereas cable and satellite are funded from a mixture of advertising and subscription.

Both the BBC and ITC have to produce a mixture of types of programme. In 1996, the BBC's output was: 31% news, documentaries and information; 15.5% films and series; 14% sport and outside broadcasts; 13.5% family programmes and light entertainment; 11.1% education; 8% drama; and 2.2% religion. The independent television companies have a similar output when Channel 4 programmes are included.

The influence of the media

Some sociologists believe that the media are used by the Establishment to influence people's behaviour. They claim that almost everyone in the top positions in the media belong to the ruling group. They went to public schools

Good news

The first great example of investigative journalism occurred in Britain in *The Pall Mall Gazette* in 1884, when the editor, W. T. Stead, showed that there were young girls being used as prostitutes in London by procuring one himself. Stead was charged by the police and served a term in prison. However, his news story led to the passing of the Criminal Law Amendment Act of 1885, which improved the protection of children. This case is used by journalists to illustrate the role and power of the press. They feel that it is the duty of the press to expose behaviour that is unacceptable to society and that, in a democratic society, the press has the power to hurt the rich and powerful if they are behaving in unacceptable ways.

and pass on to the public the ideals of a bourgeois society through the media. The media encourage people to follow certain ways of life and to buy certain goods. Capitalist society is always portrayed in a good light, even in programmes such as soaps and sitcoms.

Other people believe that the media's use of sex and violence has an influence on behaviour. Some psychologists have claimed that the rise in sex crimes and crimes of violence can be directly linked to the rise in the portrayal of sex and violence in the media. (For example, the young boy killers of James Bulger were alleged to have been watching, and possibly copying, a very violent film.)

However, others believe that although the media clearly have some influence, otherwise advertisers would not use them, the audience has just as much effect on the media as the media have on the audience. *The Simpsons* is one of the most popular shows worldwide, but it makes fun of capitalist society. Television and newspapers are in competition and need to keep their viewers and readers. If a programme does not attract viewers, it will be dropped, showing that it has not had the intended influence on the audience. *The Sun* had supported the Conservatives until 1996, when it saw that most people were now supporting Labour. It changed its support to Labour to keep its readers, rather than to influence them, in the same way that it adopted 'Page 3 girls' to attract a mass male readership, but is beginning to change this as it fears it might now lose readers because of it.

You should also be aware that TV and newspapers have been responsible for uncovering lots of things the government and capitalists would like to keep secret, such as the 'cash for questions' scandal in the Conservative government of 1992–97.

Some experts feel that there are now so many different elements to the media that the audience can pick and choose, so that they have more influence on the media than the media have on them.

Bias in the media

It is often argued that the media are biased. This is closely connected to the influence of the media. Most newspapers have a particular political bias (i.e. they support one of the political parties). It is also claimed that certain television programmes are biased for or against a political party (e.g. that *Panorama* is biased against the Conservatives and *Today* on Radio 4 is biased against Labour).

'Bias' means a prejudiced view. In the media, it occurs when one side of an argument or one point of view is given an unfair advantage by lots of coverage or ignoring its bad points. Bias can be very difficult to uncover, but a typical example is the word 'terrorist' compared with 'freedom fighter'. If a newspaper calls someone a terrorist, this predisposes the reader to think that their cause is wrong, whereas calling them a freedom fighter predisposes the reader to think that they are right.

Media ownership

Many people are worried that the ownership of the media is in the hands of too few. Rupert Murdoch, through his News International Corporation owns *The Sun*, *The Times* and BSkyB, as well as newspapers and television stations in Australia and the USA. This is now a typical situation as communications multinational companies develop. People think that someone like Murdoch must be able to manipulate public opinion and that he is too powerful to be opposed by governments. He was regularly consulted by the Conservative prime minister, Mrs Thatcher, and Tony Blair was criticised in 1999 for discussing Murdoch's commercial interests in Italy with the Italian prime minister.

However, Murdoch was banned by the ITC from making a bid for Channel 5, and when he refused to publish a book on China (because it was critical of the Chinese government and his companies were just about to sign a deal with China), it provoked an outcry and was criticised not only in the rest of the media, but also by *The Times*, which Murdoch owns. The UK does have monopoly laws that prevent any one company owning too much of the media, but the arrival of the Internet is going to make it much more difficult for any group to manipulate people through the media.

Figure 22.1 The journalist who took this photo regarded it as legitimate news because one of the prices of fame is that anything that famous people do is news

① Use the Internet to discover the names of the Sunday national papers, their circulation figures, their owners and what other papers they own.

② Use the Internet to discover the Channel 3 TV stations, who owns them and how near their owners are to the legal limit of 25% of ITV advertising revenue ownable by any one company.

③ Use the Internet to find one recent case referred to the Press Complaints Council, why it was referred and what was done about it.

④ Video the news on BBC1, BBC2, Channel 3, Channel 4 and Channel 5 on the same night. Watch them, noting the differences in coverage of the same story and stories carried by some channels but not others, and suggest reasons to explain the differences.

⑤ Try to find any notes you have on media bias from your GCSE English course.

Specimen exam questions

AS 'Outline the various ways in which the tabloid press may need to be regulated.' (You may find parts of Issue 20 and Figure 22.1 useful for your answer.)

A2 With the advent of satellite and cable television and the increasing development of specialist channels, what is the case for retaining a government-subsidised corporate service such as the BBC?

Area...**3**

SOCIETY, POLITICS AND THE ECONOMY

23

The nature of society

The *Oxford English Dictionary* has eight different definitions of society, showing how difficult it is to define the nature of society exactly. The study of the nature of society (how society originated, what it is for and how it works) is called 'sociology'. Auguste Comte first used this word in 1834 to describe the 'science of society'. He thought that this science would discover the social laws controlling the development of the human race, in the same way that the physical sciences discover the physical laws controlling the development of the earth.

Some sociologists follow Comte and believe that sociology is a science. They claim that by applying scientific methods of observation, theory and experiment to society, it is possible to discover social laws. Such sociologists are called positivists because they think of society as an objective fact, like a rock or a plant.

Other sociologists believe that sociology is about discovering how people interpret the world and how people interact with each other to form social groups. This is called 'phenomenology'.

The nature of society according to positivists

Some positivists are known as *functionalists*. They believe that each area or institution within society (such things as education, the family, and the legal system) has a function in relation to the whole of society. They often compare society to the human body and institutions to the parts of the body. Just as the heart maintains the body by pumping blood round, so the family maintains society by training children to become members of society (socialisation). The function of an institution is to contribute to the maintenance of society and to provide some of what society needs to keep it going (see Figure 23.1).

Society's needs include such things as shelter, food, socialisation and value consensus, which are often called 'functional prerequisites'. 'Value consensus' means a general agreement about what the values of society are. For example, in western society there is a value consensus that everyone should have a good supply of material goods, so the economic institutions provide a large range of goods and the family is organised to buy increasing numbers of those goods (e.g. CD players, camcorders, fitted kitchens).

Any society needs its members and institutions to be integrated if it is to flourish. Functionalists think that value consensus is the main means of social integration, but this is backed up by social control. Society controls the behaviour of its members by norms, which can be either formal or informal. Formal norms are the rules and the method of imposing the rules often uses rewards or positive sanctions (e.g. promotion at work) and punishment or negative sanctions (e.g. imprisonment) to maintain these norms. Informal norms are such things as dress codes (wearing different types of clothes for work on a building site from work in an office), which are imposed by informal sanctions (smiles, frowns or comments).

Figure 23.1 Functionalism

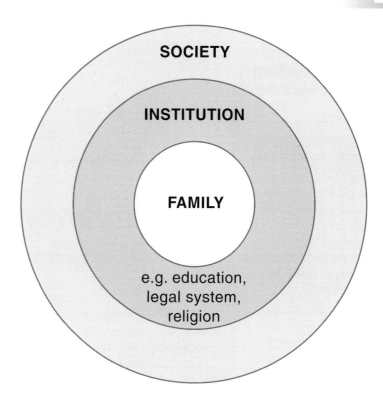

SOCIETY

INSTITUTION

FAMILY

e.g. education,
legal system,
religion

KEY words

Alienation feeling yourself no longer a part of society

Anomie not sure what the norms of society are and so feeling unhappy and lost

Bureaucracy an organisation (especially government) whose operations are full of written rules and a hierarchy of officers

Capitalism an economic system in which the means of production are privately owned

Cycle of deprivation where the social problems of one generation are passed onto the next through the family

Demography study of population changes

Hegemony where one class or group controls another, e.g. bourgeois hegemony

Labelling connected with stereotyping, it claims that people label others into certain groups on the basis of such things as appearance

Marxist ideology the belief that capitalists will try to increase their profits by paying low wages until the workers revolt and form a workers' state

Means testing only giving benefits after assessing the income and wealth of the person applying for the benefit

Peer group a group of similar age and social characteristics

Secularisation the decline in importance of religion, with political and social institutions taking on the importance formerly given to religious institutions

Functionalists accept that there can be conflicts between different groups in society, but feel that the institutions of an effective society will soon settle these, because social groups have more in common than they have differences. This is why some people claim that civil wars are only likely to happen in the less materially advanced countries, because even the poorest people in an advanced society have an interest in maintaining the electricity supply, the water supply, television broadcasts, etc.

However, there are other positivist sociologists who take a different view of society. *Marxists* believe that society is based on conflict rather than value consensus. Karl Marx believed that the history of society is based on one group being in control until their control is challenged by another group. Marx claimed that in industrial society the controlling group is the *bourgeoisie* (the owners of the means of production), which is trying to control the *proletariat* (the workers) to keep it from taking control. Marx claimed that society is based on economics, especially the 'forces of production' (the technology, raw materials, etc. involved in producing food, clothes, cars, etc.). The ruling class is always concerned to own the means of production. Marx was an economist and political philosopher rather than a sociologist, but Marxist sociologists have used his theories as a basis for their 'conflict theory of society'.

Marxist sociologists claim that the social institutions of society (what they call the superstructure) are used by the ruling class to keep the proletariat from revolting and taking control. They reflect the interests of the rulers rather than the workers and so there is a basic conflict. For example, educational institutions teach the ideology of the rulers and prepare children to perform

On the breadline

There are three different ways of deciding whether people are poor:

1 by making a list of what is necessary to live – so many calories and proteins per day, clean water, shelter, heating and cooking sources, medical facilities – so that anyone below this level can be said to be in 'absolute' poverty

2 by working out the average income of a society and the normal expectations of this average (e.g. a television and video, an annual holiday) anyone who is 20% or so below this can be said to be in 'relative' poverty

3 by asking people whether they consider themselves to be poor; if they do and their behaviour reflects this, then they are 'subjectively' poor.

the functions that will make money for the ruling class; the law is designed to protect the interests of the ruling class. (For example, the laws on property usually protect the owners of property more then the interests of groups such as ramblers.) Such sociologists explain value consensus in society by the idea of 'false consciousness'. This means that the ruling class is able to use such things as education and the family to make workers believe the ideology of the rulers (e.g. getting a mortgage and a car to give profits to the banks and car makers), when it is really in their interests to reject the ruling ideology and adopt a Marxist ideology (see 'Key words').

The nature of society according to phenomenologists

Most phenomenologists are called *interactionists*. Functionalism and Marxism may have differences, but they agree that society is made up not only of people, but also of institutions and systems, which have a great impact on the behaviour of individuals. Interactionism is completely different because it claims that society is made up of individuals who work out their role in society through interaction with other individuals rather than being forced into roles through institutions such as the family and education. Consequently, society for interactionists is always changing, as people negotiate their role in society.

The nature of society according to philosophers

Philosophers would agree with interactionists that society is made up of individuals living and working together. However, they believe that any society needs laws so that people can live and work in peace. Once this happens, social institutions will be formed and society becomes a mixture of individuals and institutions. Clearly, the institutions will have functions because that is why they arose, and there is a sense in which the institution is greater than its members (your school or college was there before you started and will still be there when you leave). However, individuals do have choices about their roles and society and its institutions change through individuals changing their roles.

So, philosophers would see society as a mixture of functionalism and interactionism, but would tend to reject Marxism because, since individuals changed society's institutions into more democratic forms, there are lots of ways in which society can be changed without conflict.

How sociologists discover facts about society

Sociologists use a variety of tools to study society.

Social surveys

These are usually conducted either by questionnaire or interview. To be absolutely accurate they would have to survey everyone in the population, but as this is impossible they should use either random sampling (which requires a large sample to make sure that all opinions are covered) or quota sampling (where the census figures are used to work out how many people in the population are in certain groups – 40–50-year-old male working class, for example – and the relevant representative quota is interviewed). Surveys have many problems, not only concerning the numbers of people interviewed (mathematicians claim that the minimum is 11 per 100 000 of population), but also in the avoidance of bias in the questions or the interviewers.

Statistical studies

These include census records and *Social Trends* (an annual publication of government figures on such things as marriages, births, employment; see Figure 23.2). Though these are more accurate than surveys, they cannot be accepted without question because there may still be some bias, e.g. when suicide was a crime, many suicides were not recorded as suicide to save hurting the family.

Figure 23.2 Children looked after by local authorities by type of accommodation, 1994 and 1998 (with permission from *Social Trends 2000*, National Statistics © Crown Copyright 2000)

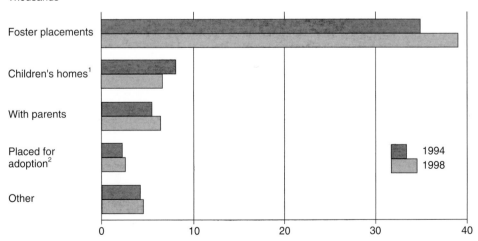

England, Wales & Northern Ireland

Thousands

[1] In England includes local authority, voluntary sector and private children's homes.
[2] Not collected for Northern Ireland.

Source: Department of Health; National Assembly for Wales; Department of Health and Social Services, Northern Ireland.

ACTIVITIES

① Imagine you have been asked by the government to investigate the effects of poverty on family life. How would you carry out the research and what methods would you use? (You may find the information in Figure 23.2 useful.)

② By questionnaires or discussion, investigate whether there is a value consensus among people you know about an issue such as car ownership versus public transport.

③ Do you think that married couples should be given greater tax benefits than single people? You should think about the importance of the family in society and use information from Issue 31 ('Economic theories') on taxation.

Observation

Sociologists watch how a group works, either by conducting a fly-on-the-wall documentary, where the observer simply watches unobtrusively, or by participant observation, where the observer pretends to be a member of a group (e.g. to investigate football hooliganism). If a sociologist wants to investigate the behaviour of a group, this may be the best method, but it has many drawbacks in terms of reliability.

Specimen exam questions

AS   Some social attitudes and values change from one generation to the next, whereas others appear to remain fairly constant. To what extent do you expect your standards and priorities to differ from those of your parents? In what areas would you expect them to remain the same?

A2   What is meant by the term 'underclass' in Britain and what implications does this have for social and economic policies?

24

Social change

Social change means the ways in which society has and is changing, and also what possibilities there are for change in a society. Many types of social change are dealt with in other issues. This issue will look at social change in terms of the family, social class, ethnicity, gender and demography.

Demographic trends in the UK

Demography is concerned with the statistics of births and deaths and population changes. When the first official census was taken in 1801, the population of the UK was 12 million; in 1997, it had risen to 59 009 000.

The UK's population grew rapidly in the nineteenth century, but slowed down in the 1920s and 1930s, perhaps because of a combination of economic depression and the new availability of contraception. After the Second World War there was a 'baby boom', but by the 1980s the UK's birth rate had fallen more quickly than the death rate, so that the population was only increasing very slightly (indeed between 1974 and 1978 the population actually fell).

As the birth rate has fallen, so the death rate has declined (see Figure 24.1).

Another trend has been for the population to move southwards. In the Industrial Revolution, it was the North of England which recorded big increases in population. However, since the collapse of heavy industry in the 1970s and 1980s, the South of the UK has experienced big population growth as people moved to jobs in the high-tech sector. This has been even more marked in Scotland (population 5 107 000 in 1997), Wales (population 2 927 000 in 1997) and Northern Ireland (population 1 601 000 in 1997). Eighty-three per cent of the UK's population lives in England and about 70% of that lives south of the Wash.

As the population has moved southwards, it has also moved out of the cities. Although the population of the South East has risen fantastically in the past 30 years, the population of London has actually fallen. People have moved into the countryside in search of better living conditions. This was begun by the government after the Second World War, when a New Towns policy was begun to build integrated living and work areas using the latest designs and ideas. The largest of the new towns is Milton Keynes in Northamptonshire, which was built to take in people from London.

In the nineteenth century, the UK had more people immigrating than emigrating as there was a great demand for workers, and Britain had a tradition of taking in religious and political refugees. Between 1890 and 1955, the UK was a net exporter of people as economic problems led to massive migrations to the USA, Australia, New Zealand and Canada. In the 1950s, a shortage of labour for British industry led to workers being recruited from the new Commonwealth countries (India, Pakistan, Bangladesh, West Africa and the Caribbean). Many of these workers had fought for the UK in the Second World War (there were more people from the Commonwealth than from the UK in the British Armed Forces in the Second World War). As these workers have settled, the UK has become a *multi-ethnic society*. Even so, in the 1991 Census, only 4.8% of the UK's population came from ethnic minorities.

Figure 24.1 (a) Birth rate and death rate and (b) life expectancy figures from 1961 to 1977

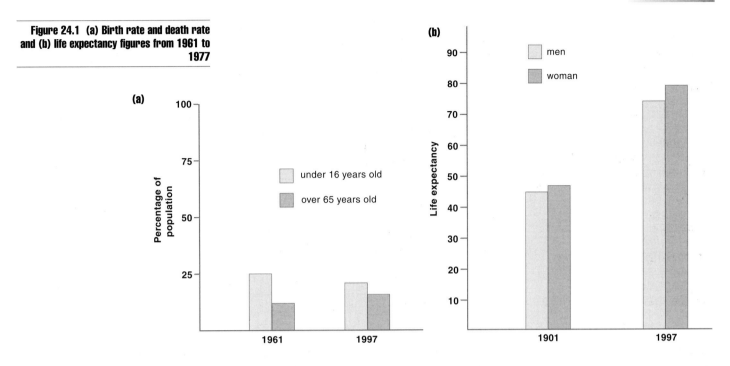

Figure 24.2 Population drift in Scotland, Wales and Northern Ireland

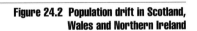

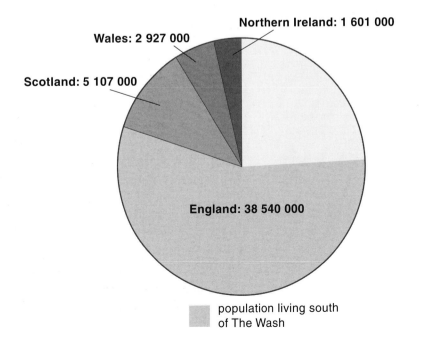

Northern Ireland: 1 601 000

Wales: 2 927 000

Scotland: 5 107 000

England: 38 540 000

population living south of The Wash

Baby boomers people born in the period 1946–53, when there was a very rapid rise in the number of births

Bourgeois members of the middle class and/or property owners

IMR infant morality rate – the number of babies who die before the age of 1 year per thousand births

Intergenerational mobility children moving social class compared, with their parents

Intragenerational mobility people moving social class through their working life

Meritocracy a system where the top jobs are given to people on the basis of their talents and qualifications (merits) rather than their birth, wealth or school they attended

Official census a survey of the whole of the UK's population carried out by the government every 10 years (1991, 2001) – every household has to fill in a questionnaire

Proletariat the working class

Registrar-General the civil servant in charge of the official census

Social class there are many views of social class from the basic upper, middle and working classes to the Registrar General's social classes 1–5. This classifies class 1 as professional, e.g. doctors and accountants; class 2 as intermediate, e.g. policemen, nurses; class 3 (a) as skilled non-manual, e.g. office workers; class 3 (b) as skilled manual workers, e.g. plumbers; class 4 as semi-skilled, e.g. postmen and bus drivers and class 5 as unskilled.

The implications of these trends

Demographic trends have major implications, especially in terms of government policies. The *ageing population* trend has implications for the National Health Service (NHS). An ageing population is going to require the NHS to take a greater proportion of government spending. There are also major implications for the Social Security budget. If people live for longer after they retire, this means that there will be more pensioners in relation to the working population. This may mean that there will be insufficient working people to pay the pensions. This is connected with the current trend of reducing the age of the workforce by giving workers early retirement. Pensions have to be worked out on the basis of how long the pensioner is expected to live. If pensioners are living 5 years longer, then it may be sensible to require people to retire at 65, or even 70. There are also housing and social service issues when seaside resorts on the South Coast consist of almost 50% of people over the age of 65.

The *southward drift* has major implications for housing and transport. More houses will need to be built in the South, putting pressure on the Green Belt. Greater numbers of people will also lead to much more transport congestion, leading to the issue of whether to increase public transport or to build new roads. Further implications are that schools and hospitals in the South are likely to be overcrowded, whereas those in the North will have surplus places. Government policies aimed at encouraging businesses to move away from the South are already in place and may have slowed down the drift.

The *rural drift* also has implications. People moving into the countryside are likely either to commute to work in towns or to be retired, but wealthy. This pushes up house prices, causing another drift away from the rural areas by people born in those areas who do not have high paying jobs. There are problems of rural deprivation as the newcomers are likely to drive to town supermarkets, doctors, etc., so that the less well-off living in rural areas suffer depleted facilities as village shops and schools close down.

The development of the UK as a *multi-ethnic community* has many implications because it is so varied. According to the 1991 census figures only 4.8% of the UK's population is made up of ethnic minorities; however, these ethnic minorities are not evenly spread. The immigrants of the 1950s settled where the jobs were, and where they were able to obtain housing; consequently, there are areas with very high percentages of ethnic minorities. Racism cannot be allowed in a multi-ethnic society as it is likely to destabilise the society. Successive British governments have tried to deal with this, leading to the Race Relations Act and the Commission for Racial Equality, both of which aim to remove racism from the UK and to give all citizens an equal chance. However, the Stephen Lawrence Inquiry Report of 1999 showed that this still has a long way to go.

Other social trends

One major trend of the twentieth century was for women to have greater participation in work and politics and for men and women to have *equal rights* and status. It was not until 1928 that women gained the same rights as men in voting and becoming MPs; it was 1970 before women had the right to the same pay as men for the same work; it was 1975 before it was made illegal to discriminate against people on grounds of sex. As a result of these changes, the workforce of the UK in 1997 was 14 708 000 men and 11 959 000 women. Such changes also have implications in terms of childcare and the nature of the family.

The nature of the family has been another area of social change. Marriage has become less popular (there were 405 000 marriages in 1971 and only 292 000 in 1995), while divorce has become more common (2.1 per thousand population in 1961, 13.5 per thousand population in 1996). By 1996, 25% of couples in the UK were cohabiting rather than marrying, and 35% of babies were born outside marriage. As a result of these changing attitudes, whereas in 1971 92% of families had two parents, by 1990, this had gone down to 81%. Some sociologists and moral experts have used these figures to suggest that the family, as it has been known during the twentieth century, will almost disappear in the twenty-first century.

The development of a classless society has also been a feature of the twentieth century. The introduction of the *Welfare State* (pensions, sick pay, unemployment pay, free education and equal access to examinations and higher education, the National Health Service) by the Liberal governments of 1906–14 and the Labour government of 1945–51 removed absolute poverty and led to the rise of a meritocracy. The restriction of the power of the House of Lords in 1911 (the Lords had prevented independence for Ireland on several occasions between 1884 and 1911), the reform of the Lords in 1999, and various policies between 1945 and 1999, led to a reduction of the power and influence of the aristocracy at the same time that the media revolutions led to the rise of the new aristocracy of pop stars, TV and film stars and sports stars.

How equal is British society?

At first sight it might appear that major changes have been made. In 1911, 5% of the population owned 87% of the nation's wealth; by 1990, that figure had reduced to 40% of the nation's wealth. However, that is still a large imbalance, which may be increasing due to changes in capital transfer tax and inheritance tax making it possible for people to hand down more of their wealth to their children. *Social Trends 29* (published by HMSO) compares the average gross income of the UK's population for 1996/97 in fifths and shows that the average gross income for the bottom fifth was £7080, while that for the top fifth was £45 870.

There is evidence from the latest government statistics that people from the lowest two-fifths of the income divide are much more likely to have lower educational qualifications, more health problems and lower life expectancy. A

Did you know?

Family first

In a 1997 government questionnaire about attitudes to the family, 88% of people agreed that children should expect help from their parents even after they have left home; 70% agreed that people should keep in touch with close family members even if they have little in common; 56% agreed that people should keep in touch with other relatives such as aunts, uncles and cousins; 48% agreed that people should turn to their family for help before going to the state.

Afro-Caribbean	495 000
Indian	787 000
Pakistani	428 000
Bangladeshi	108 000
Chinese	125 000
African	112 000
Mixed	287 000
European/Australian	472 000

Table 24.1 *Ethnic minorities in the UK in the 1991 census*

① Use Social Trends 30/31 or the Internet to find the latest figures on births, marriages and deaths in the UK.

② Interview people from different age groups and educational backgrounds to discover what they feel about social class in the UK.

③ Research cases such as the Stephen Lawrence inquiry to discover background material on attitudes to race in the UK.

④ To what extent would you agree that the UK is an equal opportunities society?

government report published in 1999 also showed wide regional variations not only in income and house prices, but also in education, health and life expectancy (income in London was 23% above the average GDP, while in Northern Ireland it was 19% below). There is also evidence that black people are more likely to be in the bottom two-fifths, are more likely to be arrested and are more likely to be sent to prison if they are convicted.

Specimen exam questions

AS 'Having two married parents offers children the best and happiest future.' Evaluate the arguments for and against this claim.

A2 In the 1990s the number of pensioners began to exceed the number of wage earners in the UK. What problems is this situation likely to create and what steps might be taken by governments, voluntary societies, or individuals to resolve the problems?

Crime and deviance

Why do people commit crimes?

Crime refers to those activities that break the laws of the land and that are subject to official punishment. It is a fundamental characteristic of all human society that, however just and reasonable a system of laws might appear to be, there will always be some individuals in a tribe, clan, school, club, religious group, country, etc., who will break it, irrespective of the severity or leniency of the the punishments. The reasons why this should be the case are a matter of strong debate amongst many sections of society. It is obviously a crucial question. If the causes of crime could be discovered and removed, this would be a much more positive course of action than to punish people after the crime has been committed. It is always better to eradicate a disease, rather than just respond to the symptoms.

Many of the background conditions mentioned in Figure 25.1 may lead to boredom, anger, envy, etc., mental states that may result in a particular crime being committed.

Crime and deviancy

What is deviancy?

In general, what is described as deviant behaviour is decided by society itself. The American sociologist Marshall Clinard defined deviance as 'behaviour which is in a disapproved direction'. This means that behaviour acceptable in

Figure 25.1 Some possible explanations for crime

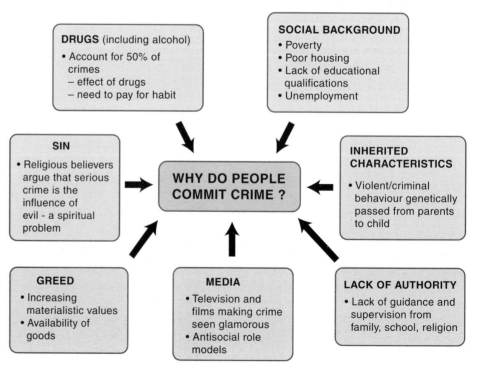

one society may not be so in another. For example, drinking alcohol is regarded as a serious offence in strict Muslim countries but is acceptable in others. Also, ideas about acceptable behaviour change over time. For example, attitudes to homosexuality have changed during the twentieth century among large sections of society. In addition, some forms of behaviour that may not be acceptable to certain sections of society may be acceptable to others. This implies that we should be careful not to categorise certain forms of behaviour as deviant or criminal too readily. Most definitions of deviance relate to laws drawn up by only certain sections of society, i.e. powerful middle-class groups. Their norms of behaviour (table manners, for example) may be alien to other sub-cultures in society and hence are not universally agreed. Once we have labelled certain actions and those that carry them out as deviant we develop stereotypes, reinforced by the media, by which we categorise individuals. The effect of this is often to change the self-image of the criminal so that he/she is forced into the role created by society.

For example, constant social rejection and failure to be offered work may change the self-image of ex-prisoners, unmarried mothers and homosexuals, so that they begin to see themselves as criminals and outsiders.

Biological/physiological explanations of deviancy

These types of theory tend to assume that criminals indulge in deviant or abnormal behaviour, which can harm individuals and be socially disruptive. Since their behaviour is abnormal, they must be sick and the solution to their problem lies in diagnosing their illness. In 1876, an Italian physician, Cesare Lombroso, argued that criminals were 'throwbacks' in the evolutionary process who not only behaved in a primitive, savage way, but could be distinguished by certain physical characteristics. These included long arms, narrow foreheads, thick skulls, etc. Lombroso argued that those who fitted this description should be carefully monitored from birth and then exiled for life when their criminal tendencies showed themselves. There is no scientific evidence for this, but there is an obvious danger that people's behaviour will be pre-judged simply because of their appearance. However, some researchers claim to have found evidence that mesomorphs (stocky, rounded individuals) tend to be particularly active and aggressive and therefore more likely to commit crimes. Other evidence suggests that a statistically significant number of violent antisocial men have an extra Y chromosome instead of the usual XY combination. Similarly, too much sugar in the blood – hyperglycaemia – may lead to criminal behaviour. Of course, it does not follow that everyone suffering from any of these conditions will necessarily become a criminal, but only that there is a disposition that may encourage deviancy.

Psychological explanations of deviancy

These theories tend to explain criminal behaviour in terms of mental states. The psychologist Hans Eysenck suggested that there was a link between genetically based personality characteristics and criminal behaviour. Personality traits such as those belonging to an extrovert are more likely to lead to law-breaking because extroverts like excitement and taking chances, and are naturally impulsive. They are also harder to socialise so that they fit in with society's

Did you know?

Law and order

White-collar crime. Crimes committed by high-status professionals such as bank managers, stockbrokers, lawyers, etc. are far less likely to lead to arrests and convictions than those committed by working class delinquents, even though such crimes can involve massive financial losses.

Many crime statistics are highly suspect. Many crimes involving personal injury such as mugging, rape or domestic violence, are not reported by the victims. Many small crimes are not recorded officially at all by the local police force.

Despite the figures, crime is equally spread throughout society. It is just that vandalism, theft, burglary (working-class young male crimes) are easier to detect than sophisticated frauds involving money.

Crime an activity that breaks the law of the land and is subject to official punishment

Deviance actions or attitudes that do not follow the norms and expectations of a particular social group

Deterrence the view that people will be put off committing crimes if the punishments are harsh enough

Subculture certain norms, attitudes and values distinctive to a group and different to those of society as a whole

Delinquency acts committed by young people, which are considered as antisocial or criminal

Retribution the theory that criminals are responsible for their actions and should be appropriately punished

Rehabilitation the view that many criminals are 'sick' and therefore, need therapeutic treatment rather than punishment

values and rules. John Bowlby argued that children deprived of close, intimate, loving relationships with their mother during early childhood may develop psychopathic personalities, displaying no remorse or guilt and little response to punishment.

Some sociological explanations of deviancy

Functionalism

Functionalists tend to argue that the source of deviance lies in society as a whole, rather than in the biological or psychological nature of the individual. Emile Durkheim suggested that crime was an essential and inevitable part of society for the following reasons:

- Not all members of society are equally committed to the shared values of that society.
- Deviance helps to bring about change in society, so it has an important function. Without some deviation from the norm, there would be no such thing as progress. On the other hand, too much deviation can stop society functioning properly, hence the need for sanctions.

Structuralism

Some sociologists argue that many criminals develop their deviant behaviour because of the way in which society is structured. Some young people belong to sub-cultures, which have developed different values from mainstream society. These values can develop because of educational, employment and financial deprivation and can result in people using criminal means by which to achieve high social and financial status.

Such situations could include:

- young men who steal and joyride expensive cars in order to bolster their own status in the eyes of their peers;
- persistent stealing to enhance the image of the thieves in the eyes of their own sub-culture – the 'respect' earned is far more important than the value of the goods stolen.

Crime and punishment

Despite the huge research, there does not appear to be a consensus of opinion about the most effective way of deterring crime or of which factors are most influential in shaping criminal behaviour. It does not follow that *all* criminal actions are caused by deep psychological states over which the criminal has no control, so that he/she cannot be held responsible or punished for his/her actions. On the other hand, the fact that many poor, unemployed, badly housed people do not commit crimes does not lead to the conclusion that these factors have no bearing on why some people become criminals.

Why do prisons fail in their aim to help offenders to return to and cope with society?

Despite the popular conception of prisons as becoming more and more like 'rest-cures' or 'holiday-camps', recent reports have described many prisons as seriously overcrowded, inhumane and uncivilised places, with insensitive and destructive regimes. If 70–80% of offenders return to prison, then prisons obviously fail, except in the areas of revenge and protection of society. Many sociologists and criminologists have argued that prisons are the breeding grounds of criminals – universities of crime, where offenders have their self-image of deviancy reinforced and where the possibility of reform is virtually

Figure 25.2 Boys, 14, bragged of killing, jury told (Newcastle Journal, 26 October 1999)

The **Journal**

Boys, 14, bragged of killing, jury told

TWO 14-year-old boys boasted to classmates about bludgeoning a man to death with pieces of wood, a court heard yesterday.

The teenagers, who cannot be named for legal reasons, killed 26-year-old Mohammed Aslam in a park in Bedford for "enjoyment", Luton Crown Court was told.

Mr Aslam's body was later discovered at about 9.15am on April 22 this year lying near a tree house beside the River Ouse.

The two youths, now aged 14 and 15, from Bedford, have denied murdering Mr Aslam the evening before.

James Hunt QC, prosecuting, said the pair had run from the scene laughing after the attack and bragged about it in school next day.

He told the jury: "Child A said, 'We had a mad day – we murdered someone,' while Child B told friends, 'We had a really wicked day yesterday'."

He went on: "These two have lured a drunken man into an area of parkland under some trees and battered him to death with pieces of wood.

"Sadly, it seems they had some enjoyment out of doing so."

Mr Aslam had been sitting drinking on a bench in the park earlier in the evening when he was approached by the two teenagers, added Mr Hunt.

Various accounts stated that Mr Aslam had either followed the youths or been chased by them to a spot underneath a tree house in a copse of willows where pieces of wood were lying around.

When interviewed by police, Child A said the man had mistaken Child B for a girl and asked for a kiss.

Child B responded by kicking Mr Aslam in the groin, while Child A began attacking him with a piece of wood.

Unmarried Mr Aslam, of Kempston, Bedford, had lived in Britain for about seven years after emigrating from Pakistan.

ACTIVITIES

① If you were a magistrate who had to sentence two young men caught joyriding and crashing a stolen car, one of whom comes from a financially comfortable home and the other from a vandalised housing estate with high unemployment, would you punish them both equally? What reasons would you use to defend your decision?

② In small groups, read the newspaper article on the murder of Mohammed Aslam and then discuss the following questions.

   • To what extent do you think that the behaviour of these two boys can be explained by any of the theories you have just been studying?

   • What punishment do you think these two boys will receive?

③ 'Television is responsible for the increase in crimes of violence.' To what extent do you think this statement is accurate and why?

impossible. Prisons often reinforce the criminal behaviour they are designed to punish or inhibit by gathering together in tightly segregated and alienated groups those who already feel marginalised, and giving them the opportunities to teach one another the skills and attitudes of a criminal career. This is particularly true of young offenders, who may find themselves mixing with hardened criminals.

Specimen exam questions

AS What explanations can you offer to account for the prevalence of crime amongst adolescent males? What might be done to reduce the amount of crime committed by this group?

A2 Discuss the view that persistent criminals are equally victims of their circumstances and that little is achieved by sending them to prison.

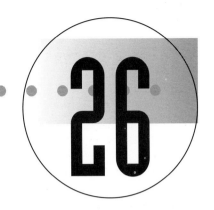

26

Educational issues

Education is a difficult word to define exactly. Almost the entire population has been to school and, in a sense, this entitles everyone who has been through the experience to express an opinion. At an individual level, education can refer to the process by which people develop their intellectual, emotional and social skills. It can also refer to the entire system of schooling within a country from nursery to university.

What are schools for?

Underlying the many sociological explanations about what schools actually do, it is usually agreed that schools have two major functions:

- to educate students in various academic or cognitive skills and knowledge
- to educate students in the personal and social skills necessary to function successfully in society.

In democratic societies, education provides the possibility of equality of opportunity and achievement. In theory, students are given the chance to do well, whatever the disadvantages of their social background. However, educational thinkers are often divided into those who think that education should serve the needs of the individual and those who think that it should serve the needs of society. In more wealthy societies, there is often an education system that reflects both these aims. Private fee-paying schools have tended to encourage individualism while, in the past, state education for the masses has emphasised the need for well-trained workers with skills relevant to the industrial demands of society. Within this framework, countries such as France and Germany have also emphasised intellectual development while Great Britain has traditionally regarded character building as as an important objective of the educational process.

Some important views on education

In his influential books, *The Republic* and *The Laws*, Plato (427–348 BC) argued that philosophers should be kings. In a turbulent and unstable historical context, Plato was trying to produce a blueprint for a stable, well-ordered society in which people fulfilled the roles and functions for which they were most suited. Only those capable of understanding and discovering the real truth about things and distinguishing true knowledge from opinion and illusion should be rulers or guardians of society. However, as the development of this ability depended on a rigorous and demanding intellectual training, only a few would be successful and the rest would occupy lower but nonetheless important positions in society. Plato's views have been very influential in the history of western education. Many education systems still reflect the views that:

- intellectual pursuits are somehow superior to practical and technical ones
- education should involve such processes as selection, segregation, assessment and rejection, in order to sort out potential leaders and followers.

John Locke (1632–1704) argued that the mind was like a blank sheet of paper at birth, 'a tabula rasa', devoid of innate ideas, which would acquire knowledge through experience. He emphasised the qualities of virtue, wisdom and learning amongst others. His view that 'experience' was essential to the educational process has remained very significant. The experiences or learning opportunities pupils are presented with at school may have a significant influence on their future success or failure.

In *Emile*, published in 1792, *Jean-Jacques Rousseau (1712–1778)* argued for a much more natural type of education. Rousseau was not impressed by the values of the civilised society in which he lived. He wanted an education system that valued and enhanced 'natural' qualities such as spontaneity, freedom, subjectivity and simplicity, rather than the cold, impersonal values of scientific objectivity and rationalism. Feeling is much more important than thinking for Rousseau who objected to the way in which children's development was 'over-intellectualised' at an early age. Rousseau's views have been the foundation of the debate between those *'traditionalists'* who argue for reason, discipline and authority in education and those *'progressives'* who want a system more sensitive to the idea of individual growth and development.

Karl Marx (181--1883), together with Freidrich Engels, argued that many human beings were alienated and dehumanised by the fact that the ruling classes owned the means of material production, even though it was the workers who created the wealth. Marx emphasised that the economic dimension of life was primary and that religious, political and educational values reflected the values of the ruling class. Marx wanted an education system that would produce responsible and autonomous persons who would work towards the idea of 'community' through social relationships. Marx had a vision of a system that would develop the idea that the interests of the individual and those of society are the same. However, many of his educational ideas have been distorted by Marxist or Communist societies, which have produced education systems that indoctrinate their students to accept the ideas of those in power without question and which discourage freedom of thought.

The social aspects of education

All education systems reflect the values and ideas of the particular society that produces them, so there is a sense in which all education is 'social engineering'.

However, some of the social functions of education seem to be essential if society is to survive.

The transmission of culture

Schools are often described by sociologists as 'agents of cultural transmission'. Without such institutions as schools, it would be difficult for civilisation to progress because every generation would have to relearn the important artistic and practical skills and the knowledge of their ancestors.

KEY words

Behaviourism a view of human learning processes particularly associated with the psychologist B.F. Skinner, who argued that actions could be 'programmed' or shaped by a system of rewards and punishments in order to produce a desired pattern. Skinner argued that human freedom was an illusion and that, in fact, all our behaviour was the result of such programming

Standardisation a type of educational management that emphasises uniformity in school procedures including what is taught, the pattern of the school day and how children are assessed

National curriculum introduced in 1988, it specifies the amount of time pupils should spend every week on maths, english, science, etc.

Parental choice the view that parents should be able to choose which type of school their children should attend

Schooldays

The *1988 Education Act* initiated the following changes:

- regular school inspections

- a Qualifications and Curriculum Authority to oversee national examinations and the curriculum

- the extension of parents' right to choose schools

- the freedom of schools to 'opt out' of local authority control.

Deschooling society. In the 1970s a series of educational thinkers argued that most education systems were a waste of time. Most pupils leave school uneducated and resentful. Schools are a type of prison, operating on the assumption that education can only take place inside mass institutions and adults assume that they know what is best for young people.

Formula funding. Money for schools is based on the number of pupils enrolled. An increase/decrease of 20–30 pupils can mean the addition or loss of one teacher.

The transmission of values and beliefs

All schools transmit to their pupils, whether deliberately or not, some sense of what is acceptable in terms of behaviour and attitudes. Schools emphasise the idea of achievement through personal effort and perseverance and also community values, such as honesty and consideration for others. In some education systems, the prevailing religious beliefs of the country are built into the curriculum. There has been a strong Catholic emphasis in Irish schools in the past and religious education with a strong Christian emphasis is compulsory by law in the UK. On the other hand, in France and the USA, for example, religious teaching is forbidden. However, many school systems encourage patriotic feelings and emphasise democracy. Recently, some school boards in religiously conservative parts of the USA refused to allow the use of textbooks that taught Darwin's theory of evolution on the grounds that it contradicted the account of creation in the book of Genesis.

Preparation for life

Traditionally, one of the most important functions of schools has been to prepare its students for a place in society. Modern governments are concerned to produce a work force with relevant and up-to-date skills so that the country can compete economically in the international market place. This requirement has resulted in different ways of organising schools and in legislation to ensure that all children receive some education. In the UK, for example, most local authorities operate a system that involves primary education until the age of 11, followed by non-selective comprehensive education until the age of at least 16. This may be followed by voluntary post-16 education either in a school sixth form, a purpose-built sixth form college or further education college, or as a preparation for university. A few local authorities still retain selective grammar schools (where the children sit an exam at 11 to decide whether they are clever enough to go to grammar school) and others operate a three-tier system, where children move from first school to middle school and on to secondary school at the age of 13. New technology colleges have also been introduced which emphasise computer and technological skills.

Which system is best?

Those who argue for selective grammar schools believe that children do better in separate institutions, which cater specifically for their needs. Academically gifted children perform better when surrounded by peers of similar ability and avoid the risk of distraction by less motivated and academically talented pupils. Many parents claim the right to pay for this opportunity for their children. Those in favour of comprehensive education argue that such a selective system is socially divisive. Those who do not pass entrance examinations to such schools often carry a sense of failure all their lives. Comprehensive schools, in theory at least, encourage children from different socio-economic and cultural backgrounds to work together and to develop social cohesion. Comprehensive schools should provide educational opportunities that cater for the needs of individual pupils within the same institution.

Educational assessment

Although many parents judge the success of a school by its academic results, recent research has shown that such factors as the economic status of the school catchment area and parental support can have a significant effect on academic performance. Schools in very economically deprived areas find it difficult to persuade their pupils or their parents that education is of value, either because it may lead to employment or because it trains the mind. Good public examination results do reflect academic success, but the emphasis on such results often hides the genuine progress made by pupils whose gifts are not recognised by the examination system itself.

Figure 26.1 A Victorian schoolroom – Shepton Mallet Grammar School, Wiltshire, 1899

① A school with poor examination results is a bad school. What reasons would you use to either support or oppose this statement. What other information would you need to know about the school?

② Which of the following is the most important part of school and why: the child; the curriculum, assessment?

Specimen exam questions

AS How important and useful do you consider the new Key Skills and General Studies to be in post-16 education? How effective and essential are they in promoting greater breadth of study in the curriculum?

A2 To what extent do you think that the main purpose of education should be to prepare young people for the world of work? What do you consider the main purposes of education to be? Which do you regard as the most important?

The nature of law

There are various aspects of human life to which the word law might be applied. Practically speaking, 'law' refers to a body of regulations enacted by parliament that are meant to maintain and enforce the general welfare of society. The word 'law' can also be used in science to refer to regular, uniform and predictable sequences of events. Scientists use phrases such as 'laws of nature' to describe such things as gravity or the conservation of matter. The phrase 'natural law' is also used by some religious and ethical thinkers to suggest the idea that there are certain ways of behaving that fit in with how things ought to be and certain states of affairs that do not. For example, 'cloning' might be described by some as being against 'natural law'.

Why do we need laws?

Human beings are social creatures – they tend to live together in groups. During the thousands of years over which societies have developed, human beings have learnt that survival of the group depends on the development of a system of law. Law could be described as a way of structuring the tension between the self-interest of an individual within a group and the interests of the group as a whole. Anthropologists, historians and others who study primitive societies point out that whatever the cultural differences between different groups, they all have laws about such matters as protecting the elderly and weak, bringing up children, marriage, property rights and violence.

In a simple, small society, the population can decide its own laws and pass judgment on its lawbreakers. However, in larger, more complex societies, not only do the laws themselves become more complicated, but politicians have to be appointed to make the law and lawyers, judges and police are needed to interpret and enforce the law. In this situation, the law is often seen as something imposed by the authorities from 'outside', or from 'above', rather than a system of rules agreed to by every member of the community. However, most people would agree that, in general, the law provides a secure framework for society, in which human beings can flourish and exercise personal moral choice. Also, the law, in theory at least, protects the weak and vulnerable from those likely to exploit them.

Examples of laws

One of the earliest known systems of laws comes from the reign of Hammurabi, ruler of Babylon in 1790 BC. One example of his laws is, 'If a man blind a freeman in one eye, he shall lose his own eye.' At first glance, this law looks like a commendable attempt to deal with violence in a just manner. However, by using the word 'freeman', it implies the existence of slaves. By definition, slaves have no rights. The idea of justice, on the other hand, suggests equality and fairness for everybody. This raises the question of the relationship between law and justice. Also, this law makes no distinction between a deliberate or an accidental act. Laws tend to be very general, as it

KEY words

Civil disobedience a protest by a group of citizens, usually peaceful but involving illegal action against a state of affairs to which they have moral objections, e.g. hunt saboteurs and anti-abortionists

Committal proceedings a preliminary hearing, in front of magistrates, to decide whether there is sufficient evidence for the case to go to Crown Court for trial

Common law this applies to laws that may be interpreted by judges in court when they have to decide on difficult or obscure cases. It also refers to ancient customs and usages that have almost acquired the status of law.

Constitutional law the collection of statutes passed by acts of parliament down the ages. There is no one definitive written constitution in Great Britain

Counsel a lawyer qualified to represent a client in court, usually a barrister

Indictable offence an offence for which a person can be tried by jury

Judicial system the system of courts and sentencing designed to deal with civil and criminal offences

Justice of the Peace a magistrate

Lord Chancellor a member of the government and the House of Lords who is the head of the court system in the UK

Social justice the application of fairness and equal treatment to all members of a society

would be impossible to describe every possible situation in advance. Another issue raised here concerns the problem of violence. Should the state show its' disapproval of violence by engaging in further violence? This is an important question when discussing such issues as capital punishment.

Another famous set of laws is The Ten Commandments, which appears in the Old Testament. It is claimed to be of divine origin and probably originates from before 1200 BC. One of these laws states, 'You shall not kill'. This is obviously an essential requirement for any civilised society, but it raises many problems in interpretation. For example, does it mean that violence is ruled out in all circumstances? Does it rule out defending oneself, one's family or one's country against unprovoked attack? Does it rule out helping an elderly suffering relative who asks voluntarily for euthanasia?

Why obey the law?

Any civilised society needs *civil laws* to decide issues concerning property, taxation, child custody, etc. and *criminal laws* to deal with violence, theft, fraud, etc. Most people recognise that obeying the law produces benefits.

- In general, it produces more good than harm for society; for example, settling disputes by legal means tends to avoid the use of violence.
- Obeying the law sets a good example for others and avoids a gradual decline into chaos.
- Obeying the law means that people know what to expect from each other, which is essential for trade.
- Breaking the law requires law enforcement and punishment costs money, which will have to be provided by the community.

Disobedience and the law

The compulsory wearing of seat belts or the fluoridisation of water supplies are modern examples of legislation. In both these cases, it is argued that individuals have to give up their personal right to choose in the interests of society as a whole. Seat belts save lives, and not wearing them could cost the NHS a lot of money, therefore everyone must wear a seat belt. Successful laws are probably those that manage to keep a balance between the interests of individuals and those of society. However, it is clear that there may be examples of unjust laws and this raises the issue of whether disobeying the law can ever be justified. The mediaeval theologian, *Thomas Aquinas* (1224–1274), argued that an unjust law was not a proper law. However, most thinkers accept that there may be unjust laws and deal with the question of whether they can be disobeyed.

In 399 BC, the Greek philosopher *Socrates* was unjustly condemned to death by the Athenian council on the grounds that he was subverting the state and corrupting the young with his radical ideas and questions. Despite the attempts of his friends to persuade him to escape from prison, Socrates refused, on the

grounds that if one accepted the benefits of the state, so one had to abide by its decisions. Even though the verdict of the court was unjust in his particular case, the social consequences of disobedience would be far more damaging as a whole than the injustice suffered by one man. Socrates was not against all forms of disobedience, however. He also argued that if someone believed that the laws of a state were corrupt then he had the right to disobey any that affected him.

John Rawls (1962) argued that any system of justice and law is to do with the concept of 'fair play'. If people agree to abide by this and recognise that it is socially necessary for everyone to obey the law then it is not fair if someone decides to disobey the law because it is to their personal advantage. Provided that the injustice is not too great or unfairly distributed, Rawls argued that we have to accept some unjust laws. According to Rawls, the injustice of a law is not sufficient reason for disobeying it.

The American philosopher *Henry Thoreau (1817–1862)* argued that people's actions should be governed by justice and not by legality. Civil disobedience can be justified if the law is seen to be an agent of injustice. Thoreau rejected the idea that civil disobedience would lead to social unrest and revolution by suggesting that this state of affairs would actually be caused by governments resisting reform. Governments should listen to those who point out examples of injustice, rather than trying to crush their protests.

Martin Luther King (1929–1968) was one of the most famous exponents of civil disobedience. Through his campaigns of non-violent resistance to racist laws and conditions in the USA, King brought about changes to the law and established the *Civil Rights Movement*. He argued that those who obeyed their conscience and refused to obey a corrupt or unfair law were not showing disrespect for the law but the opposite. They were recognising the difference between just and unjust laws and expressing their support for law and justice. Racists, however, were prepared to support unjust laws because they benefited a minority, thus putting personal advantage ahead of justice.

Law and punishment

All societies have systems of punishment in order to support their legal codes. There are various justifications for such punishment.

- *Retribution.* According to the retributive theory, criminals should be punished because they deserve it. This theory is based on the idea of justice so that people who have done something wrong get their just deserts. The theory also says that criminals should be punished in proportion to their crime so that serious crimes receive a greater punishment than less serious ones. The problem is in deciding which crimes are more serious than others and what is an appropriate punishment.
- *Deterrence.* This theory justifies punishment on the grounds that a long prison sentence for an armed robber, for example, may deter others from committing the same crime.

- *Rehabilitation.* This approach concentrates on the needs of the offender rather than on the offence itself. The purpose of the sentence imposed is to change and reform rather than to punish. It also assumes that there may be all sorts of background circumstances that have influenced the behaviour of the offender, so that they may not be entirely responsible for their actions.
- *Protection.* This involves the permanent detention of some offenders on the grounds that their release might put ordinary members of society at risk.

Many of these theories overlap. For example, life-imprisonment deters, protects and inflicts retribution. It is extremely difficult to decide which criteria are the most important. Some murderers have made one bad mistake, are horrified by their past actions, represent no danger to society but are serving long sentences, while other criminals, such as armed robbers, are full of hatred and violence and will inevitably re-offend but are serving short sentences (see also Issue 25, 'Crime and deviance').

Parliament enacts laws. The police force enforces the criminal law. The court system interprets the law and decides on guilt or innocence. The English system is based on the 'adversarial model'. In criminal cases, it is prosecution versus defence, while in civil cases it is plaintiff versus defendant. In all adversarial systems the judge acts as referee and interpreter of the law. In civil cases, the judge decides on blame or guilt and in criminal cases this role is taken by the jury, composed of 12 electors under the age of 65.

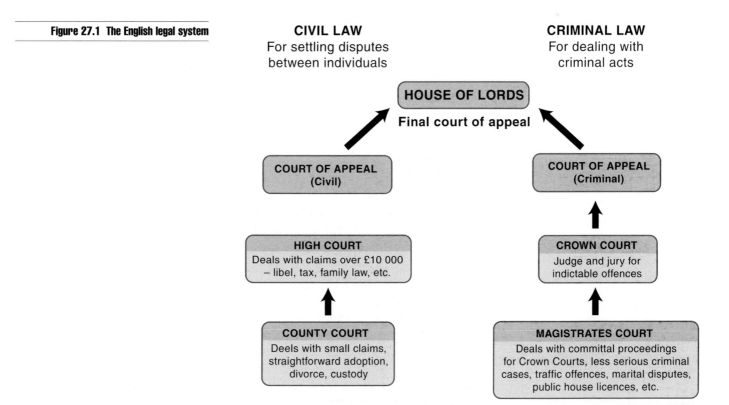

Figure 27.1 The English legal system

CIVIL LAW
For settling disputes between individuals

CRIMINAL LAW
For dealing with criminal acts

HOUSE OF LORDS
Final court of appeal

COURT OF APPEAL
(Civil)

COURT OF APPEAL
(Criminal)

HIGH COURT
Deals with claims over £10 000
– libel, tax, family law, etc.

CROWN COURT
Judge and jury for
indictable offences

COUNTY COURT
Deels with small claims,
straightforward adoption,
divorce, custody

MAGISTRATES COURT
Deals with committal proceedings
for Crown Courts, less serious criminal
cases, traffic offences, marital disputes,
public house licences, etc.

Figure 27.2 Tree protestors objecting to the building of a new runway at Manchester airport

Activities

① In small groups, describe six serious crimes which have been in the media recently. List them in order of seriousness, giving reasons for the order. What punishment would you consider appropriate for each of these crimes and why?

② A recent television series included a group of animal rights protesters who planted bombs that killed two people. Do you think such illegal action can ever be justified and why?

③ Over 60% of first-time offenders return to prison. Do you think prisons should emphasise punishment or rehabilitation and why?

④ List the occasions when you think it would be reasonable to break the law, giving your reasons.

Specimen exam questions

AS Why is it necessary to punish offenders? Outline the main options and discuss the effectiveness of the various forms of punishment available to an English Court of Law.

A2 Pressure groups sometimes take 'direct action' in order to make their case known. To what lengths should protestors be prepared to go to promote their cause? In what circumstances can extreme or illegal actions be justified?

Power and control

'Power' can be defined on a personal level as the ability to get one's own way, even when others are opposed to one's wishes. From a wider perspective, power is about who has the authority and the capacity to change states of affairs in a society. Politics is often defined as the struggle to acquire and exercise such power. Sociologists often distinguish between two forms of power: authority and coercion.

- Authority refers to the exercise of legitimate power, which is accepted by everyone as right and just. For example, parliamentary decisions are accepted as lawful by members of society because they accept Parliament as having legitimate authority.
- Coercion refers to the exercise of power that is not regarded as legitimate by those subject to it. Members of the Republican Movement in Northern Ireland, for example, do not accept the authority of the British government and so regard the exercise of their power as coercion. Coercion may involve the use of force to overcome opposition.

The sociologist Max Weber suggested that there were three types of authority:

- Charismatic authority derives from those exceptional qualities displayed by some leaders which enables them to produce intense loyalty, admiration and obedience in their followers. Examples of such powerful leaders include Alexander the Great and Napoleon.
- Traditional authority refers to the acceptance of certain customs and traditions which have been long established. Accepting the authority of a reigning monarch because of his/her inherited status would be an example of this.
- Rational/legal authority is based on the fact that all the members of society accept a legal framework with a particular shared end in view. In general, people accept the authority of the legal system because they realise that it serves the goal of justice.

There is also what might be referred to as the authority of expertise. We tend to accept the authority of those whose expertise we recognise – doctors, teachers, solicitors, etc. Accepting their authority often means accepting their right to give us instructions.

Why do we need power?

Human beings tend to be gregarious (inclined to live in groups). The fact that virtually everyone lives together in groups immediately raise problems about how such groups should be organised. For example, the idea of 'government' usually implies either a group or an individual who is in control of the affairs of a nation. However, the way this control is exercised has profound effects on the lives of the population. Under some forms of dictatorship, a 'political discussion' might take the form of indoctrination, which justifies the authority of those in power and stifles opposition. On the other hand, you might argue that although in a democracy everyone has the right to express their views, the complicated nature of the democratic process itself prevents people's views from being heard.

Anarchy a state in which there are no institutional forms of government

Universal suffrage the right of virtually all adults to vote in political elections

Freedom of information the idea that there should be no government secrets

Legal aid a government financed scheme to pay the legal costs of less well off people so that the rich cannot control the poor in the legal system

Lobby to try to influence a Member of Parliament

Meritocracy a form of government in which a self-appointed elite of the most knowledgeable and capable people rule

Oligarchy a state in which the government is in the hands of a small group

Republic a state without a monarchy

Totalitarianism a type of government that allows no opposition to its policies or the existence of rival parties – found in extreme Fascist and left-wing countries

Important questions raised by the discussion of power include the following:

- Who should govern and by what means?
- By what right do they exercise authority and control?
- What activities should governments be involved in?

What is a government?

A government is an organisation that has the authority to make and enforce rules and laws about important and extensive areas of human life. However, it is only a legitimate government if its authority is accepted by everybody. A government that makes laws that no one accepts, but which forces people to obey it through military might, is not a proper government because its right to enforce laws is not recognised by society. Many other organisations in society, such as labour unions, large corporations, religious institutions and schools, etc., exercise authority over sections of society, but what makes governments significant is the extent of their authority. This may include such areas as law and order, education, social welfare, defence, taxation, immigration.

The purpose of government

Most political thinkers agree that some form of government is necessary and preferable to a state of *anarchy* in which there is no institutional government whatsoever. The justification for needing some form of government includes the following reasons:

- to *serve the interests of the most powerful*. This is the cynical view that government is just an organised form of domination. The most powerful group uses government agencies as a means of serving its own interests.
- to *protect people from one another*. This is the most common theory about the purpose of government. Without laws and the means to enforce them, some people would treat other people very badly and subject them to theft, personal violence and other forms of abuse. Governments exist to construct and establish a legal and social system that will provide a secure environment in which economic production and culture can flourish.
- to *promote God's will*. This ancient theory argues that governments exist to carry out the will of God and their authority consists of the fact that the government is the earthly representative of God on earth. This type of view can still be seen in some religiously fundamentalist societies.
- to *develop and control the economy*. This type of theory is particularly associated with *Marxism*. According to Marx, the purpose of government is to promote the expansion of the forces of production by finding more and more effective ways of producing goods. In the final stages of history, ordinary workers finally own the means of production and control the government so that policies are all aimed towards the general welfare.

Power to the people?

Elite theorists argue that even in advanced democratic countries such as the UK, political decisions are actually taken by a small group who share similar social backgrounds. For example, 80% of Mrs Thatcher's last Cabinet had been privately educated.

In *The Prince*, a treatise on how to govern, *Niccolo Machiavelli* (1469–1527) argued that those who wield power should be like 'lions and foxes'. Lions achieve and maintain power through forceful decisive action. Dictators are examples of lions. Foxes, on the other hand, rule through cunning and diplomatic wheeling and dealing.

John Locke (1632–1704) argued that human beings have inalienable rights, including the right to free speech, religious belief and the right to property. Governments are appointed by the majority to preserve these rights. Locke had to flee abroad because of these democratic and anti-monarchic views.

- *to bring about equality*. This theory is based on the assumption that people should have equal opportunity and equal status in a society. It is the role of government to prevent artificial social or economic distinctions and to eliminate all inequalities of property, money, achievement or power.

In practice, most governments carry out a range of functions, some of which are conflicting. While most democratic governments try to act in the interests of the general welfare of society, this may involve attacking the rights of some individuals. For example, forcing people to pay taxes or to engage in compulsory military service is an attack on individual freedom, which is justified in terms of the good of society as a whole. There is a wide range of political views concerning the extent to which governments should exercise control over people's lives. *Socialist* political thinkers tend to argue that governments should own the agencies that provide education, housing, health, transport, power etc. because these are all essential to the welfare of human beings. *Free-market/libertarian thinkers* tend to argue that governments should exercise as little control as possible in peoples' lives and that people should provide for their own welfare.

Who should have control?

The most widely accepted view is often referred to as *the consent of the governed*. A government gets its power from the fact that the people of a particular country consent to it acting on their behalf.

- The *American Declaration of Independence 1776* not only specified the purpose of government as the protection of natural rights and the promotion of people's happiness, but also claimed the right to abolish the authority of a particular government if it was not pursuing those purposes.
- *Thomas Hobbes (1588–1679)* argued that in their natural state the lives of men were 'solitary, poor, nasty, brutish and short'. In order to avoid a lawless state of nature, people agree to a 'social contract', in which they give the sovereign enough power to control people's lives. This will provide a secure environment in which goods can be produced, and people can be protected from each other. However, once the sovereign has acquired this power, it cannot be claimed back, therefore government is no longer by consent.
- *Jean Jacques Rousseau (1712–1778)* argued for a different type of social contract. Rousseau thought that human beings were naturally good and had kindly feelings for each other. However, he suggested that they need to live in society in order to develop their full potential and to do this they should enter into a social contract where they surrender their individual rights to the 'general will'. This is concerned with the good of the whole community and in large communities wise legislators have to be elected to draw up laws and policies in agreement with the general will.

Democracy

Most political thinkers would argue that democracy – rule by the majority or all of a population – is the best form of government. In a democracy, the government is elected by the free choice of the population and can be removed without violence. In a modern democracy, virtually all adults can vote, irrespective of sex or status. The principal advantage of democracy is that people can exercise direct control over their policy makers by voting them out of office. Also, policies tend to reflect the interests of the majority and so receive general support. Disadvantages of democracy include the fact that non-experts often get elected to powerful positions because they are popular. Also, in a system where the majority rules, minority interests and opinions may suffer, although some definitions of democracy include human rights and individual freedom as a part of democracy. Another disadvantage is that in a system where candidates have to appeal directly to the voters, the most charismatic and financially supported public speaker may be elected rather than the most suitable person for a particular post.

Specimen exam questions

AS   Outline the main purpose of government in a democratic society. What limits should there be to the power of a government?

A2   To what extent is it possible to claim that the law and government are designed to protect the interests of the rich and powerful in society at the expense of the poor and the weak

ACTIVITIES

① 'Power corrupts and absolute power corrupts absolutely.' (Lord Acton).
   a) Explain what you think this statement means.
   b) Use your own research (Internet or library resources) to find recent examples of corruption. This might include bribery, buying votes, rigging elections, etc.

② 'Democracy is not perfect but it is the best political system we have.' Discuss the disadvantages and advantages of democracy and say what improvements/alterations you would like to make to the present system.

29

Politics

What is politics?

One useful definition might be, 'Politics is the activity by which groups reach binding collective decisions through attempting to reconcile differences amongst their members.' The Greek philosopher *Aristotle (384–322 BC)* said that 'man is by nature, a political animal'. Human beings live in groups and they can only resolve their conflicts of interest, make plans and take decisions by engaging in some sort of political activity. In this sense, all rational human beings take part in politics even if they are not professional politicians. Politics is a complex activity, which contains the following elements, to name but a few:

- *Diversity of views*. If there were no differences between people about future plans and methods of achieving them, there would be no need for political activity.
- *Reconciliation*. One of the principal functions of politics is to find an accepted solution to problems caused by major differences of points of view.
- *Decision making*. Politics involves making decisions about future actions that will be binding on all members of a group and may be backed up with force.

Politics and government

Although some extreme political activists argue for 'anarchy' – the absence of law and government – most people recognise that in large communities individuals and institutions have to be appointed to take decisions and execute policy on their behalf. Collectively, this is referred to as the government. (Different types of government are discussed in detail in Issue 28, 'Power and Control'). Governments can loosely be divided into *authoritarian* and *democratic*. Examples of authoritarian governments include the following:

- *Military rule*. In many African, Asian and Latin American countries, military leaders took over governments in response to economic and civil problems. Many of these leaders put down opposition ruthlessly and themselves acted as a dictatorship.
- *Personal dictatorship*. Many African countries replaced colonial powers with 'hero-figures' who had fought against the colonial powers, for example, Jomo Kenyatta, President of Kenya (1962–1978) and Kenneth Kaunda, who ran Zambia (1964–1991). Both these leaders ended up as very autocratic, resistant to change and responsible for economic decline.
- *Dominant party rule*. Countries such as Singapore and Egypt appear democratic but in reality are run by one very powerful party, which controls the media, the economic resources and has the ability to rig elections.

KEY words

Single transferable vote an electoral system that allows voters to transfer their vote to where it will be most effective after the first ballot – used in Eire

Globalisation the process by which social, cultural and economic trends and policies are less dependent on national power and more influenced by worldwide issues, e.g. European currency issues

Referendum a system that allows every elector to vote directly on an important national issue, such as Scottish or Welsh devolution – an example of direct rather than representative democracy

Two-party system the traditional state of affairs in British politics, where Parliament is dominated by two strong parties with far more members than the nearest minority. This would be changed by proportional representation.

Politics in Britain

Like most Western European countries, the USA, Australia, New Zealand, etc. the UK is governed as a *liberal democracy*. This can be described as a system where elected politicians act on behalf of those who elect them but within carefully defined limits, so that the rights of minorities and individuals are protected. The most important feature of democracy is the idea of *representative government*. This includes the following characteristics:

- a *Member of Parliament* who represents the interests of their constituents
- *freedom of expression* – people can choose their representatives freely
- *sovereignty of the people*, where the will of the general population is paramount
- *political equality*, meaning that every person's vote and right to vote is of equal value.

Parliament

In the UK, the representative government is Parliament, which consists of three parts:

- *the Monarch* , who has no real power but presents the current government's future plans in the Queen's Speech at the opening of Parliament
- *the House of Lords* (in the process of being reformed), which has hereditary peers, life peers, 26 archbishops and bishops and nine senior members of the legal system, known as Law Lords
- *the House of Commons*, consisting of 651 elected members. Since 1872, Members of Parliament have been elected by secret ballot. Any member of the public can vote for any candidate without having to reveal their choice. Virtually all members belong to either the Conservative Party, the Labour Party, (the two largest), or the Liberal Democrats. Much smaller numbers represent the Ulster Unionists and the Welsh and Scottish Nationalist parties.

The process of government

In practice, the government is made up of the Prime Minister and the Cabinet, which consists of approximately 20 of the Prime Minister's senior colleagues and their assistants who have been appointed as Ministers of State to run various departments such as defence, education, transport, etc. or to represent areas such as Scotland or Wales. This group of ministers is responsible for introducing new policies that they wish to become law. These measures are known as bills until they have passed through Parliament, after which they become *Acts of Parliament* and then law. This whole process of government involves three interlocking areas:

- *Legislature*. This describes the work of Parliament which has the responsibility to make new laws and to change existing ones.
- *Executive*. This refers to the work of Ministers of State and the civil service departments they run. They are responsible for the execution of the wishes of Parliament, e.g. producing the detailed administrative framework for a change in the law affecting pensions, or raising the school-leaving age.
- *Judiciary*. This refers to the process by which expert judges settle disputes concerning the interpretation of the law.

Acts of Parliament

In order for a bill to become an Act of Parliament, it has to have three readings. The first introduction is a formality before the second reading, where the general principles of the bill are discussed by those present in the Commons at the time. This is followed by the committee stage, where the details of the bill are examined in depth before it is sent back to the Commons for a third and final debate. Although in theory it can then be held up by the House of Lords, it will eventually become law despite their opposition, as long as a majority vote for it in the Commons. The formal Royal Assent of the sovereign is then required for it to become law. In practice, very few bills introduced by a majority government fail to become law.

Criticisms of the system

Although in theory the political process in the UK appears to be very democratic, various important weaknesses have been highlighted in recent years.

The problem of oligarchy

Oligarchy means 'rule by the few'. In the House of Commons, very few backbench MPs have any influence on government policy or the opportunity to introduce a bill dealing with the interests of their constituents, because of the pressure on parliamentary time. Backbenchers may be appointed to parliamentary select committees to examine various issues, but in general, they are there to vote in accordance with party wishes. This gives the Prime Minister enormous *patronage* (the power to grant favours, including promotion in response to loyalty). Legislation is controlled by the Prime Minister and the Cabinet.

Adversarial politics

In the House of Commons, the government benches face those of the Opposition. Debates in the House tend to emphasise criticism of the other major party, and the manipulation of the process in order to gain narrow political advantage, instead of emphasising important national and social

Did you know?

Vote for me

- *Parliamentary Select Committees* were first established in 1979 to scrutinise the performance of government departments and ministers.
- In a recent election, the Conservative and Labour parties spent £30 million on election expenses between them.
- *The Single European Act, 1986* established the concept of free movement of goods, services and persons and the removal of physical, technical and fiscal barriers to free trade.
- *The Royal Society for the Protection of Birds* has more members than the Conservative, Labour and Liberal Democrat parties put together. This raises the question of how far the traditional political parties actually represent the views of most of the electorate.

interests. Because of the shortage of parliamentary time, bills can be 'talked out' by opponents using up all the time available to pass a bill through to the next stage, sometimes involving an all-night sitting.

Conflict of interest

Unlike the USA, where the written constitution guarantees a clear distinction between the different processes of government, there has been a tendency for recent British governments to interfere with the judiciary and the executive branches of government. High-ranking members of the civil service, which is supposed to be impartial, have been replaced by people sympathetic towards government policies, and senior civil servants have been overruled by government 'advisers'. The government also has a strong influence in the appointment of bishops and judges.

The electoral system

Proportional representation

Under this system, a large number of candidates would stand in each constituency and according to a special formula, votes of the least supported candidates would be transferred to stronger ones. This would eventually

Figure 29.1 Votes and seats in the 1997 election

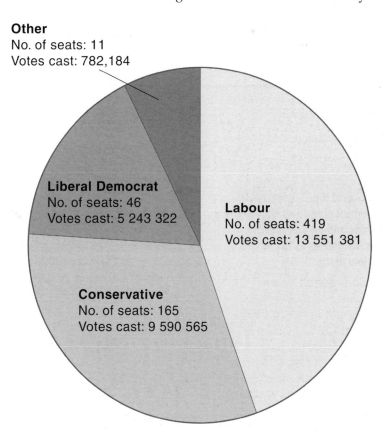

Other
No. of seats: 11
Votes cast: 782,184

Liberal Democrat
No. of seats: 46
Votes cast: 5 243 322

Labour
No. of seats: 419
Votes cast: 13 551 381

Conservative
No. of seats: 165
Votes cast: 9 590 565

① Read the extract below from Lord Hailsham. What improvements do you think might make the parliamentary system more democratic?

'I have reached the conclusion that our constitution is wearing out. Its central defects are gradually coming to outweigh its merits, and its central defects consist in the absolute powers we confer on our sovereign body [Parliament], and the concentration of these powers in an executive government formed out of one party which may not fairly represent the popular will.' (Lord Hailsham, 1976 Dimbleby Lecture)

② What might be the advantages and disadvantages of closer ties with Europe?

③ Do you think Members of Parliament should be allowed to vote according to their conscience or should they always obey the party line?

④ Do you think the establishment of separate Welsh and Scottish assemblies would divide the UK or help to bring it together?

ensure that members elected represented the number of votes cast and a much wider range of members would be elected. This would be a more representative electoral system, but it might make strong government more difficult because of the reduced possibility of a large majority for any one party and the need to accommodate a wide range of interests when making policy.

First-past-the-post

A democratic electoral system should ensure that the majority rules and that significant minorities are represented. The present system elects the candidate whose voters are in the majority in a particular geographical area. This means that a particular party may become the government because it has the most members returned in a particular election, but does not represent the total numbers of voters nationwide. In the 1987 election the Conservative Party had a majority of 102 members but had only polled 43.4% of the total vote. Under the first-past-the-post system, the government is formed by the strongest minority rather than a genuine majority. Parties such as the Liberal Democrats are under-represented in Parliament because their support is distributed evenly across the country, but not concentrated in any particular area. This means that they end up with fewer parliamentary seats than they are entitled to by their total vote.

Specimen exam questions

AS   Discuss the importance of *each* of the following in determining the results of a UK general election: electoral system; media; opinion polls; image of the party leaders; manifestos of the political parties.

A2   There appears to be an increasing apathy in Britain towards politics and politicians, as indicated by recent poor turn-outs in local and European elections. How do you account for such apathy and does it represent any danger to democracy? How might people be encouraged to play a more positive and active role in politics?

The British Constitution

Bicameral an assembly with two chambers, the lower directly elected. The upper may have different methods of membership

Bill of rights a written document that lays out the rights of citizens in a state. It might include freedom of religious belief and practice, freedom of speech of the press, assembly, and in the case of America, the right to bear arms

Judicial review the power of special courts to rule on the legality of the constitution. This includes ruling on the legality of specific actions by the government, resolving conflicts between the state and an individual over civil liberties and deciding conflicts between different government departments

Legislature this refers to the law-making function of a particular assembly. In the UK, parliament is the supreme law-making body

It is hard to define the concept of 'constitution' and even harder to define the British Constitution. However, a generally accepted view is that, 'a constitution sets out the formal structure of government, specifying the powers and constitutions of central government, sets out the balance between central and other levels of government and specifies the rights of citizens'.

There are written and unwritten constitutions, with most modern countries having a written constitution. The constitution of the USA is contained in 7 pages, while that of India is several hundred pages long. It is usually claimed that the British Constitution is unwritten, but there are several written parts of it:

- *The Bill of Rights, 1689* is the basis of the British Constitution. It was written to justify the way in which the leaders of Parliament had removed King James II from the throne. By declaring various practices of James II illegal, it made the British monarchy constitutional. It stated that the monarch cannot raise taxes, pass or suspend laws or keep an army without the consent of Parliament. It set down rules for the length of Parliaments and for free elections to them. It also gave all British people the right to freedom of religion and MPs the right to complete freedom of speech in the House of Commons.
- *Habeas Corpus 1679* compels the authorities to bring anyone arrested before the courts, so preventing what is known as 'arbitrary arrest', where people can be arrested and kept in prison without trial.
- Various *Representation of the People Acts* have been passed so that now, by law, everyone over the age of 18 has the right to vote and parliamentary constituencies are arranged so that a similar number of electors elects each MP.
- *The Act of Settlement, 1701* stipulates that the monarch and the monarch's spouse must be Protestant (James II was a Catholic). This is a sign of the way in which Parliament is in control of the monarchy, but also reflects the fact that the monarch is also the Head of the Church of England, which is Protestant.
- *The Parliament Act of 1911* removed the power of the House of Lords to do anything but delay legislation approved by the House of Commons.

All political power is based on the Prime Minister and the Cabinet. The monarch must act on their advice. The Cabinet controls all the government departments (run by the civil service) and the armed forces. However, the courts are independent of the government (though the Lord Chancellor who selects judges, is a member of the government) and citizens can challenge the government through the courts (including the European Courts) if they believe the government is acting illegally.

There are other checks and balances on the power of the government. If the Prime Minister loses a vote of confidence in the House of Commons, he or she must resign. They must also hold an election at least every 5 years. The monarch could remove any Prime Minister who refused to do either of these things, and, as the armed forces and the civil service take their oath to the monarch, there would be the power to force their resignation. The monarch also has the final decision as to who to call as Prime Minister if no one party wins a majority in an election – this has never yet happened and no one knows what would happen if it did.

The British Constitution has considerable flexibility as Parliament can adjust the constitution if conditions change.

Figure 30.1 The British Constitution
(reproduced with permission from Axford,
Politics: An Introduction, Routledge, 1997)

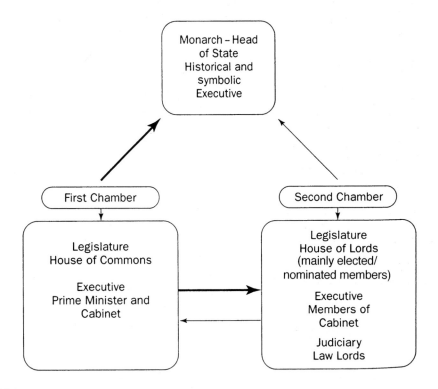

The need for reform of the British Constitution

Many political thinkers believe that the British Constitution is in need of reform. Some feel that there is a need for a complete written constitution in one document, which should also make a clear statement of the rights of individuals. Others think that the position of the monarch needs to be more clearly defined, while others think the idea of hereditary monarchy in a democracy is contradictory and so the monarchy should be abolished. Others feel that too much power is concentrated in the hands of the Prime Minister and the Cabinet and that power should be devolved, firstly to the separate nations of the UK (Northern Ireland, Scotland and Wales), then to the regions. It is also felt that the sovereignty of Parliament requires a second chamber to vet proposed legislation from the Commons, but this cannot be done by a chamber with an inbuilt majority of one political party (until the hereditary peers were removed from the Lords, the Conservatives could win any vote in the Lords).

Devolution and the House of Lords are two of the main issues surrounding the British Constitution.

Reform of the House of Lords

The UK is the only democracy to have a second chamber where the members are unelected and most of whom are there by the historical accident of having inherited a peerage. The total membership until the recent abolition of hereditary membership was approximately 1200. After the *Life Peerage Act* of 1958 allowed the government to appoint life peers of either sex, two-thirds of the members were still hereditary.

Problems with reform

Although the existence of such a second chamber cannot be justified, it has been difficult to find an acceptable alternative. Labour governments have recognised that while the House of Lords usually has a large Conservative majority, its undemocratic nature has meant that it has no real political authority to challenge legislation produced by a majority in the House of Commons. Replacing it with a large number of elected members would give it more power to resist government policy, while having too many directly appointed members would allow governments to put its own supporters in place. This would continue the political patronage, which appoints a majority of life peers who support the current government. The current debate initiated by the recommendations of the Wakeham Commission (2000) is focused on what proportion should be elected, what proportion should be directly appointed and for how long, how to bring in representatives from social and ethnic minorities, and what the total membership should be.

Devolution

Devolution refers to the process of transferring the power from ministers and Parliament to regional or sub-national bodies, which are subordinate to Parliament but directly elected. Unlike such countries as the USA or Germany, which operate a *federal* system where individual states have guaranteed status, in theory Parliament could abolish the powers of a region. For example, in 1972, the British government abolished the Northern Ireland Parliament at Stormont. The new Northern Ireland, Scottish and Welsh Assemblies are an attempt to bring about devolution and successful power sharing to recognise different national identities. Devolution has been a political issue since at least 1886, when W.E. Gladstone introduced an unsuccessful bill to give Ireland Home Rule in Dublin. The pressure for devolution in Scotland and Wales can be seen in the increased number of Members elected to Parliament who represent the Scottish National Party and Plaid Cymru, the Welsh National Party, since 1974.

Advantages and disadvantages of devolution

One advantage of devolution is that it may make government more effective and representative. This emphasis can be seen in the fact that a referendum was called for to sound out the feelings of the three populations. One disadvantage is the problem caused by the fact that Scottish Members of Parliament, for example, could sit in their own assembly and in the House of Commons. This means that Scottish Members would be able to vote on issues

Did you know?

Let's vote on this

- The UK has adopted the European Convention on Human rights into British law. Citizens can now appeal to the Court of Human Rights in Strasbourg. This reduces the sovereignty of Parliament.

- In 1979, Parliamentary select committees were introduced to scrutinise the work of government departments. Attendance is compulsory when asked.

- Since taking power, the present Labour government has appointed 200 life peers to the House of Lords in order to reduce opposition.

- The only nationwide referendum ever held in the UK was on the issue of joining the European Community in 1975.

affecting English regions, but English Members would not be able to vote on Scottish ones. Another difficult issue is whether sub-national assemblies should have the power to raise taxation. The UK has a unique structure. Scotland and Wales have their own distinctive cultures and histories. The process of devolution is an attempt to recognise this diversity by giving the populations involved a real, rather than a merely symbolic say in government. The problem is whether the devolution of real power to regional and sub-national assemblies would destroy the traditional relationship between England, Wales, Northern Ireland and Scotland so that the UK no longer exists in a meaningful way.

Figure 30.2 The House of Lords before reform

CTIVITIES

① In small groups, discuss what features you think are essential in the constitution of a modern democracy. Construct a Bill of Rights that clearly lists these features.

② Do you think that the advantages of separate Welsh and Scottish Assemblies outweighs the disadvantages and why?

③ Some MPs have been paid to ask particular questions in Parliament by powerful interest groups. Is this practice antidemocractic and why?

Specimen exam questions

AS   What qualifications do you think Members of a second chamber in parliament should have? Should they be elected or appointed by the government and in what proportion?

A2   In recent years opinion polls have indicated a gradual decline in support for the monarchy, especially among young people. Examine the arguments both for the retention of the monarchy in its present, or in a changed form, and for its replacement with a republic.

31

Economic theories

According to the *Oxford English Dictionary*, economics is 'the science of the production and distribution of wealth'.

If human beings were self-sufficient, there would be no need for economics, but as soon as a farmer could produce more food than he needed, and another farmer, who made pots, discovered that people wanted the pots he made, economics was needed so that the potter-farmer could become a full-time potter. Specialisation or division of labour (certain people producing certain goods rather than each person producing everything they needed for themselves) is one of the bases of economics. Although economics in the form of the production and distribution of wealth has been around since the beginning of society, theories of economics did not develop until the eighteenth century.

Adam Smith (Professor of Moral Philosophy at Edinburgh University) wrote *The Wealth of Nations* in 1776, in which he worked out how the human desire for self-betterment will lead to changes in society and a gradual increase in wealth. Although written over 200 years ago, Smith's book contains most of the economic theories now accepted by the vast majority of economists.

The law of supply and demand

This says that if there is a low supply of a product and a high demand, the price will rise. Conversely, if there is a high supply and a low demand, the price will fall. This is why brain surgeons are paid more than factory workers (there is a high demand and a low supply of brain surgeons; there is a low demand and a high supply of factory workers, who require less training and intelligence than brain surgeons).

Economists believe that the forces of supply and demand create an equilibrium (where supply and demand are mainly equal) through the price people are prepared to pay meeting the price for which the supplier is prepared to sell.

Market forces

Closely connected with supply and demand are market forces. The market means the place where consumers and suppliers meet. A supplier can keep the price of a product artificially high by restricting the supply, or by creating a *monopoly* (a market where there is only one supplier). However, in a *free market*, it will always be possible for another supplier to come along and offer the product at a lower price. This is known as competition and the theory of economics is known, from Adam Smith, as *laissez-faire economics*, where the role of a government is to prevent monopolies occurring so that market forces can determine prices and wages and what is produced.

There are lots of market forces that can affect the basic law of supply and demand:

KEY words

Assets things that you own; fixed assets are things such as buildings and machinery, current assets are things you can quickly sell for cash

Break-even point the point where the amount of goods sold equals the costs so that a profit is made after this point

Diseconomies of scale where a company has become so large that it is inefficient

Economies of scale where a company has become so large that it can save a lot of money by bulk buying, borrowing money cheaply, etc.

Equity capital the value of the shares in a company at the price they were first sold at (what a company owes its shareholders)

Free enterprise private ownership of capital, the market economy

Liquidity when a company has more current assets than current debts

Monopoly when there is only one producer or provider of a product

Remuneration usually wages, but whatever you are paid for providing a service

Turnover the amount a company receives for selling its products (this takes no account of costs and so is much higher than the profit)

- changes in income (if wages or taxes fall or rise, people will have less or more money to spend and so demand will fall or rise);
- changes in price of connected goods (if the cost of CD players falls, the demand for CDs will rise);
- taste and fashion (BSE caused a fall in demand for British beef; the introduction of mountain bikes caused a fall in demand for ordinary bikes);
- competition (a new firm producing the same product will increase the supply and reduce the price);
- population changes (as people live longer, and there are more people over the age of 65 in the population, there will be a rise in demand for Saga holidays and pensions).

Money and exchange rates

In the early stages of human development, specialisation was needed for civilisation to occur. However, there was then the problem of how the potter and the farmer were to exchange their surplus products. At first this was done by *bartering* (I will give you 'x' beans and 'y' chickens for 'x' plates). However, as society became more complex (How do people like teachers and poets barter?), some other system was needed. Money was developed as a system, which gave an external value to bartering.

Money has no *intrinsic value* (a pound coin has no value in itself, unlike a plate) but is based on the value or resources of the government or bank that issues the money. These resources must have intrinsic value and if that value goes down, the value of the money will go down. Money works on the law of supply and demand, so that a currency in high demand will have a high value, and one in low demand, a low value.

This can be seen clearly in the exchange rate of a currency. The exchange rate is the value given on the world markets to one currency in terms of another currency (the exchange rates of the world currencies in terms of sterling – the British pound – are on the business pages of newspapers every day). Until 1972 there were fixed exchange rates made under the Bretton Woods Agreement, 1944. This mean that everyone knew the value of goods worldwide and manufacturers exporting goods knew exactly what their profits would be. However, the drawback was that if a country was not doing as well as expected, it would have to *devalue* its currency by negotiating a new exchange rate. Since 1972, there has been a *floating exchange rate*, where the market decides the value of a currency.

If the value of a currency goes up, this means you can buy more with it abroad, but manufacturers will find it more difficult to sell abroad as their products will be more expensive. However, imports will be much cheaper (for example if the value of the pound against the euro increases by 10%, a French car that cost £10 000 in Britain will now cost £9000, but a British car of the same value will now cost £11 000 in France. This is explained more fully in the section on balance of payments in Issue 32, 'Economic problems'.

Not such a gamble?

'PLC' means 'public limited company'. This means that there is a limit to the liability of the directors and shareholders of the company. In a private company, if the company owes money it cannot repay, the company's creditors can have the owners declared bankrupt and recover their debts from the owners' private property. In a PLC, liability is restricted to the amount of shares issued. If the company 'goes bust', the shareholders lose their money, but the creditors cannot claim from the directors.

The benefits of restricting liability in this way is that it encourages people to invest in the economy knowing that they are only risking a fixed amount of money. The problems of not having limited liability were shown when Lloyds of London suffered big insurance losses in 1989 and 1990 and the names (people who invested money and had been taking big profits) had to fund the losses, with many having to sell their houses.

Figure 31.1 Mrs Thatcher, Conservative Prime Minister 1979–1992, claimed to be using the principles of monetarism and market forces to reduce the power of trade unions

ACTIVITIES

① Follow the exchange rate of the dollar, the euro and the yen against the pound for a period of 4 weeks to see whether the value of the pound is rising or falling. Establish reasons for the trend.

② Discuss why computer firms in the South East of England may have to pay higher wages to their staff than the same firms in the North East of England.

③ Imagine you are setting up a company that could produce either CD players where there are lots of other firms in the market, or a video player using CDs instead of tapes, where there is currently only one manufacturer. Give arguments for and against each option.

④ To what extent do you think that people of high ability deserve higher rates of pay? Should there be a maximum as well as a minimum wage? What overall principles should determine the financial rewards for the work people do?

Keynesianism

This is an economic theory based on the ideas of J.M. Keynes (1883–1946), who claimed that Smith's ideas on market forces producing full employment were wrong. He said that in times of high unemployment, the government should increase spending to increase national output and so increase employment. In times of full employment and inflation, governments should reduce expenditure. This was the economic theory behind Roosevelt's New Deal in America, which led to the recovery of the American economy after the Wall Street Crash of 1929 and the Depression of the 1930s.

Monetarism

This is an economic theory connected with the American economist Milton Friedman who claims that any economic problems such as inflation or unemployment are caused by the government producing too much money (the *money supply*), and that by restricting the money supply firms will have to lower wages and cut staff to become more productive. This will eventually lead to greater profits and so there will be more resources and the money supply can be increased.

Specimen exam questions

AS To what extent do you think that people of high ability deserve higher rates of pay? Should there be a maximum, as well as a minimum wage? What overall principles should determine the financial rewards for the work that people do?

A2 To what extent should the government interfere with the law of supply and demand in areas of high unemployment or in subsidising particular industries?

32

Economic issues

Economic issues are problems or arguments about issues concerning money or the state of the economy. The main ones you are likely to be asked questions about are covered in this issue.

Taxation

In any country, the government requires money to provide services. This money is raised by levying taxes on the population.

In the UK in 1999–2000, the government spent £350 billion (£6000 for each person in the country; see Figures 32.1 and 32.2).

Arguments about taxation come in three forms:

1 *Whether the taxes are being spent in the right way.* One of the main debates between political parties is how much money should be spent on *social security*. The reforms of disability allowance and the work of the Child Support Agency are aimed at reducing the amount spent on social security. Any changes in employment will affect the social security spending (the more people who are unemployed, the more benefits have to be paid out). Changes in the population can also affect the budget (an increase in the number of old people will increase expenditure on pensions and health; a decrease in children will reduce expenditure on child benefit and education.

   There are also arguments about whether more or less should be spent on defence than education, etc. Any political party that suggests that there

Figure 32.1 Tax income for the UK, 1999–2000 (source: Treasury Pre-budget Report, November 1999)

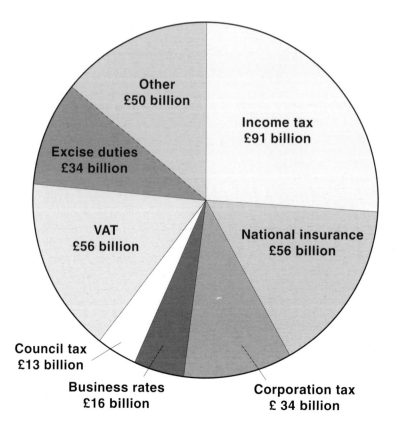

Other
£50 billion

Income tax
£91 billion

Excise duties
£34 billion

National insurance
£56 billion

VAT
£56 billion

Council tax
£13 billion

Business rates
£16 billion

Corporation tax
£ 34 billion

Figure 32.2 Tax exepnditure for the UK, 1999–2000 (source: Treasury Pre-budget Report, November 1999)

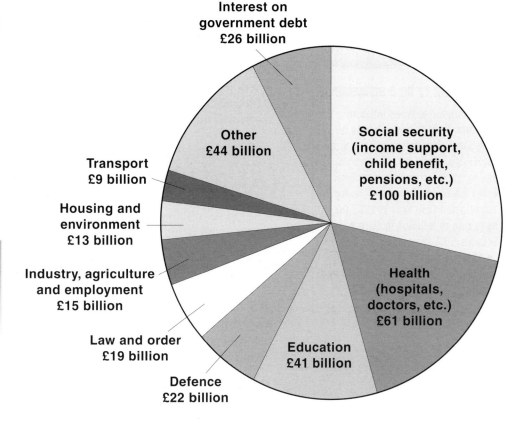

Interest on government debt £26 billion

Other £44 billion

Transport £9 billion

Housing and environment £13 billion

Industry, agriculture and employment £15 billion

Law and order £19 billion

Defence £22 billion

Education £41 billion

Health (hospitals, doctors, etc.) £61 billion

Social security (income support, child benefit, pensions, etc.) £100 billion

KEY words

Balance of payments the difference between what a country imports (buys from other countries) and what it exports (sells to other countries)

Fiscal policy decisions on taxation and public spending

GATT General Agreement of Tariffs and Trade – since 1948 the main countries have met to agree on trading with each other

GDP Gross domestic product – the total value of the goods and services produced by a country in a year

GNP Gross national product – the GDP plus any income from investments abroad

IMF International Monetary Fund

Monetary policy decisions on interest rates and the amount of the money supply

OECD Organisation for Economic Co-operation and Development established by the industrialised nations in 1961 to achieve the highest growth and living standards in member countries

Social costs the costs of producing goods, which the producer does not have to pay, e.g. the education of the workforce, the transport systems being used, the costs of the pollution caused by the production

Tariffs customs duties placed on goods being bought from abroad usually to protect the country's own suppliers

should be more police on the streets is also suggesting that the amount of taxation spent on law and order should be increased which will mean either increasing taxes, or reducing the amount spent in some other area.

2 *Whether taxation should be direct or indirect. Direct taxes* are those collected directly by the government. Income tax is a direct tax, which the Inland Revenue collects from every adult. It is *means tested* (the more you earn, the more you pay) and is a percentage of your earnings, capital gains and interest from savings above a certain allowance. *National insurance* and *corporation tax* are also direct taxes collected by the government. Council tax and business rates are direct taxes collected by the local council.

Indirect taxes are often called hidden taxes. They are a percentage of the cost of various goods, which are collected by shopkeepers, etc. and then paid to the government. *Value added tax* (VAT) is 17.5% of all goods sold in shops except food, newspapers and books. *Excise duties* are paid on petrol, alcohol, tobacco and are much more than 17.5%.

Some people claim that indirect taxes are unfair because everyone pays the same amount whatever they earn. Other people claim that indirect taxes are the fairest taxes because rich people can find ways of not paying direct taxes (some of the richest people in the country pay no direct taxes). There is no way of avoiding indirect taxes, but the rich spend more than the poor, so they will pay more taxes.

3 *What the level of taxation should be.* There are many arguments between politicians as to what percentage of the gross domestic product (GDP) should be paid to the government. Those who favour a free market approach believe

Who wants to be a millionaire?

Hyperinflation is when inflation becomes so high that it has to be calculated on a daily rather than a yearly basis, and the government has to issue larger denomination notes weekly. For example during the Yugoslavian Civil War in 1993 the daily rate of inflation in Serbia became 50% (something costing £1 on Monday cost £1.50 on Tuesday). In 8 weeks 1 million dinar notes had become 50 million dinar notes.

that the percentage should be much lower and that most people should have to pay for such things as their own health and education needs. Those who believe in a mixed economy (see below) would be happy to see taxation at between 35 and 40% of GDP because of the benefits of giving everyone the same opportunities and care. Some socialists would want much higher taxation in order to redistribute wealth from the rich to the poor, but many economists believe that if taxation is too high, people stop doing any extra work and the economy slows down.

Inflation

Inflation is the rising of prices. It is measured by the Retail Price Index (RPI), where a representative sample of things people have to buy is measured on a baseline of a particular year. This can give an annual inflation rate (the percentage by which prices have risen over 1 year).

Inflation is caused by:

- the value of the currency falling;
- pay rises not being supported by increases in productivity;
- demand for goods being greater than the supply.

The effects of inflation are:

- a rise in interest rates;
- businesses going bankrupt because they cannot afford the interest, or their customers cannot afford the much higher prices they have to charge;
- people's standard of living going down because their wages have not increased as much as the prices;
- people saving more because the interest rates are high, so they do not buy goods, so firms cannot sell goods and have to sack workers, thereby increasing unemployment.

Governments try to reduce inflation by reducing demand. They may do this by *monetary policy* (restricting credit and increasing interest rates) or *fiscal policy* (increasing taxes and reducing government spending).

Although all economists agree that high inflation is bad for the economy, some economists believe that a medium rate of inflation is better than high unemployment and lower living standards.

Types of economy

In any society there are scarce goods and scarce resources and there has to be a mechanism for allocating them.

In a *market economy*, the scarcities are allocated by market forces. The price mechanism of supply and demand is regarded as sufficient to run the economy. The market economy is favoured by right wing political parties who claim it is the most efficient way of producing and allocating goods and gives the consumer greater power.

The disadvantages are that social costs are ignored and poor people get no help. If there is no public sector health, education, etc. everything has to be paid for by the private individual buying from the private sector.

Left-wing parties tend to favour the *command economy*, where all production is in the hands of the state (private companies are nationalised). They claim that this is more efficient because people can be given what they need, income can be distributed fairly and industry can be made to be aware of social costs, e.g. by reducing pollution. The disadvantage is that by ignoring the laws of supply and demand and keeping all decisions in the hands of the government massive mistakes can be made (for example, making shoes no one wants to buy) – the Soviet Union had a command economy that collapsed, leading to the collapse of the Soviet Union, itself.

Centre parties usually operate a *mixed economy* , where there is a public and a private sector. In many ways, this is a market economy that is controlled by the government to remove the disadvantages. Public goods such as health and education are provided by the state. A 'safety net' is run by the state to provide money for those who are unwanted by the market (the old, the unemployed, the sick and the young). The government also forces firms to pay attention to the social costs of their production.

Figure 32.3 The Chancellor of the Exchequer, Gordon Brown, on budget day, 1998. The budget is the government's statement on what it intends to spend and what taxation will be for the coming year

Activities

① Use the Internet to find the proportion of taxation to GNP for the UK, the USA, France and Germany.

② Using the Internet and discussion, make a list of the arguments for and against indirect taxation.

③ Should taxation be used to implement social policies? You may like to think about such issues as the government ending the tax allowance for married couples, the government giving tax allowances for working mothers to pay for childcare, but not for the wage earner if one of the parents stays at home to look after the children.

④ How would you change the public spending and taxation figures given in the 1999 Pre-Budget Report? Give reasons for your answers.

Specimen exam questions

AS Outline the various forms of taxation available to the UK economy and consider the strengths and weaknesses of each.

A2 The end of the twentieth century saw the spectacular collapse of the communist command economies. What is the role of government and in what ways should it interfere in the running of the market economy? (In your response you should consider such issues as the provision of basic necessities – food, shelter, health, law and order, education, employment, defence.)

The European Community

In the first half of the twentieth century, Europe was the cause of two world wars, which killed millions of people and weakened European economies. After the Second World War, European leaders met to work out ways of preventing Europe ever again going to war against itself. Out of the various options, West Germany, France, Italy, The Netherlands, Belgium and Luxembourg signed the Treaty of Rome in 1957 to form the European Economic Community (EEC). The aims of the EEC as expressed in the Treaty were to:

- remove barriers to trade among member nations;
- establish a single commercial policy towards non-member countries;
- coordinate members' general economic and agricultural policies;
- coordinate member states' transport systems;
- remove all national barriers to free trade and competition;
- establish free movement of labour and capital throughout the EEC.

The first successful policies were concerned with the removal of tariffs and quotas between members, with the result that between 1957 and 1968, trade between the member states quadrupled. Indeed, the EEC was so successful that in 1973, the UK, Ireland and Denmark also joined. Greece joined in 1981, followed by Spain and Portugal in 1986. East Germany entered as part of the re-unification of Germany in 1990 and Austria, Finland and Sweden joined in 1995, after which time the 15 states became the European Community (EC).

How the EC is organised

Ultimate power in the EC lies with the *Council of Ministers*, which consists of a representative from each member government. Such meetings can be called at any time to make a decision. The European Council meets three times every year. This is made up of the heads of governments of the member states and ensures that no member state can be forced to do things it does not agree with as each member has a right of veto in the Council of Ministers (though there was some agreement at the meeting in Finland in December 1999 for limited areas where majority voting would be introduced).

Decisions made by the Council of Ministers are implemented by the *European Commission*. This is the EC civil service. The President and Commissioners (each responsible for a policy area, e.g. Neil Kinnock responsible for transport) are selected by the Council of Ministers for a 4-year term and no more than two may be of the same nationality. It is the role of the Commission to ensure that the policies of the Council of Ministers are put into practice. They also award EC grants to member states and draw up acts for the European Parliament or the Council of Ministers to debate.

The *European Parliament* has 500 members, with each member state having its number of MEPs determined by its population as a proportion of the total EC population. All MEP's have to be elected by proportional representation and the election of 1998 was the first proportional representation (PR) election in the UK. The system is completely different from all other elections in the UK being based on political party rather than personalities (see Issue 29, 'Politics' and Issue 30, 'The British Constitution').The Parliament has 12 one-week sessions during the year, but members are also expected to serve on standing committees responsible for checking the work of the Commissioners. The Council of Ministers has to consult the Parliament on various matters, but the Parliament's main function and importance is to keep democratic control of the European Commission. It has to approve the Budget of the EC and can force the resignation of commission members if they have behaved improperly (the last President of the Commission, Jaques Santer, was forced to resign by the European Parliament).

The *European Court of Justice* has 11 judges appointed by the consent of all the members states for a period of 6 years. There are many situations where EC law overrules national law and there have been several instances where individual UK citizens have taken the UK government to the European Court of Justice and the government has been forced to change policy (e.g. homosexuals being allowed to serve in the Armed Forces, men having the same rights as women to cold weather payments over the age of 60).

Main EC policy areas

KEY words

Brussels often used as a synonym for the European Commission, whose headquarters are in Brussels

ECB the European Central Bank

EMU European Monetary Union, the idea behind the euro

Federal state the idea of a European central government, with the national governments becoming similar to the state governments in the USA

Free trade the idea of countries having no trade tariffs against each other's goods, but not having common laws

National sovereignty a nation having control of all its affairs (see Issue 32, 'Economic problems', for discussion of whether this is possible in a world of multinational companies)

QMV qualified majority voting, the idea that members of the EC should not be able to use the veto to hold up progress in certain areas.

Rotating presidency the presidency of the Council of Ministers moves from one member state to another so that every state has a turn

Strasbourg the headquarters of the European Parliament (it is in France, but right on the border with Germany)

When the EEC was established, all the member states supported agriculture, but in different ways. The first major success was to bring all national agriculture policies into the *Common Agricultural Policy* (CAP). This bans all tariffs and quota restrictions between member states and a common tariff system is applied to agricultural products from non-member countries. An EC price is set for all agricultural products and if the market price falls below this, the EC buys from the farmers at the EC price. Although this policy was a major success, and made the EC agriculturally self-sufficient, it also led to huge surpluses (as farmers produced more when the price was high); these were often referred to as butter mountains and wine lakes. It has also led to conflict between countries such as the UK and Germany, which are net importers of food (and so pay into CAP much more than they receive) and Italy and France which are net exporters (and so receive much more from CAP than they pay in). One of the provisions of the Maastricht Treaty was the reform of CAP and the reduction of both subsidies and surpluses. This is a major area of concern in the EC.

Another area of concern has been that of *foreign policy*. If the EC has common economic and agricultural policies, it should have a common foreign policy. Matters of foreign policy are regularly debated at the Council of Ministers and the Kosovo intervention in 1999 showed that it is possible for all the member states to work together on foreign policy. It would seem impossible now for EC members to take different sides in a war, but without any machinery for a common foreign policy, this is still possible in theory. Several decisions were made in 1999 by the Council of Ministers that make a common foreign policy more likely.

In the same way, *defence* should be a common matter. Most, but not all, of the EC states are members of NATO, a common defence group between Europe and North America. It would appear that the EC should have a common defence policy and an agreement to defend any member state that is attacked.

Can we join your club?

The UK did not apply to join the EEC until 1961 because it did not think it would be a success. However, since 1953 the UK's production had only risen 30% compared with France's 75% and West Germany's 90%. The French President, de Gaulle, said in 1963 that the UK was not yet ready to join and so the UK's application was rejected. In 1970, the new Conservative Prime Minister, Edward Heath, applied again. France now had a new president, Pompidou, and the UK, along with Ireland and Denmark, entered the EC on 1 January 1973. The Labour Party promised a referendum on the UK's membership of the EC in the election of 1974. As they won that election, a referendum was held in 1975, when 67% of those who voted were in favour of the UK being a part of the European Community.

The *Maastricht Treaty*, December 1991, committed the EC to formulating a common foreign and security policy, but by the end of the 1990s, little had been done. The Kosovo intervention in 1999 showed the need for this and there were subsequent agreements for member states to contribute forces to a European rapid deployment force. The European defence industries now work together to produce European fighter aircraft, tanks, etc.

The *Single Market* was established by the Maastricht Treaty. This treaty established the *Single European Act* and changed the law so that all citizens of member states became European Union citizens. All restrictions on mobility of labour, exchange controls, Europe-wide banking and other financial services were outlawed. The European Monetary Institute was established at Frankfurt and the ECU (European Currency Unit) was introduced for trade between members as a preliminary to a common European Currency (the euro).

During the1990s, the collapse of the Soviet Union and its empire in Eastern Europe led to many more states wanting to join the EC – Poland, Hungary, The Czech Republic and Turkey were among the states applying to join. Politically, it would make sense for all European States to be members of the EC, but there are major implications for the euro and CAP if countries with weak economies and a high percentage of agriculture are allowed to join (e.g. it would lower the value of the euro and increase the spending and surpluses in the CAP).

The euro

A *European monetary system* was begun in 1979 to avoid day-to-day fluctuations in the money markets affecting trade between member states. This was based on the value of the German Mark and meant that members had to make sure (by interest rates, taxation, etc.; see Issue 1, 'Economic theories', and Issue 32, 'Economic problems') that the value of their currencies stayed within a percentage band of the mark. This system was known as the ERM (exchange rate mechanism) and the UK initally took part in it. However, the value of the pound declined rapidly in 1992 and the UK was forced to withdraw from the ERM.

Maastricht had set 1999 as the deadline for introducing the euro. In order for the euro to work, interest rates, inflation rates and public sector borrowing rate (PSBR) (the difference between what a government receives in taxes and spends) in states joining the euro had to be equalised (as well as the currencies being in their correct band in ERM). Those members who met the criteria and wanted to join locked their currencies into fixed parities on 31 December 1998 and on the first of January 1999 Austria, Belgium, Finland, France, Germany, Ireland, Italy, Luxembourg, the Netherlands, Portugal and Spain became part of the euro. The European Central Bank took over the functions of the national banks to control the exchange rate.

The expected benefits of the euro are:

- a currency that can compete with the dollar (the GDP of the 11 states is almost as big as that of the USA);
- a saving of as much as 0.5% GDP for member states;
- an increase in trade between members;

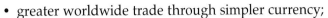

- greater worldwide trade through simpler currency;
- greater tourism between member states through a common currency.

The possible costs of the euro are:

- less freedom for member governments over economic policies;
- possibility of Europe-wide taxes rather than national taxes;
- less flexible labour markets, leading to higher unemployment;
- the possibility of economic union, leading to political union (this is only a cost to those who regard a federal state of Europe as a bad thing).

Specimen exam questions

AS What are the arguments for *and* against membership of the European Union and further integration between member states?

A2 How effective have multinational organisations such as the EU, NATO and the United Nations been in recent years? In your response you should make detailed reference to *at least one* area of conflict and assess how successfully the situation has been resolved.

① Read as much as you can in the newspapers, or use the Internet, to discover more detailed information on the arguments for and against the euro.

② Consult the Business Studies Department to find out the effects of EC legislation on business.

③ Consult the Health and Safety Committee to discover the effects of the EC on Health and Safety legislation.

④ 'Being part of a European Federal State would be better than being dependent on American multi-nationals.' Examine the arguments for and against this view.

Rich world, poor world

In 1980, world leaders expressed their concern about the growing division between the rich countries of the mainly northern hemisphere and the poor countries of the southern hemisphere. The *Brandt Report*, (named after the former chancellor of West Germany, who was its chairman) identified the difference in living standards between countries. For example, in North America living standards are forty times higher than in many parts of India and Africa. These countries are often referred to as *economically less developed countries* or *ELDCs* because they have not benefited from the effects of technology and the Industrial Revolution in the same way as the more developed countries in the north.

Poverty

The most important characteristic of ELDCs is *poverty*. It has been argued by many voluntary and United Nations aid agencies that poverty is the fundamental cause of many other problems. Poverty traps millions of people in a cycle of malnutrition, disease, illiteracy, large families, etc., often limiting their capacity to work hard enough to grow enough food to live on or to earn sufficient wages. Poverty produces powerlessness so that people are incapable of removing themselves from this cycle of deprivation (see Figure 34.1). For example, many southern hemisphere farmers only grow enough food to feed their own families. If the crop fails, they either starve or have to borrow the cost of new seed from money lenders at exorbitant rates of interest. Farmers who

Figure 34.1 The unending cycle of poverty

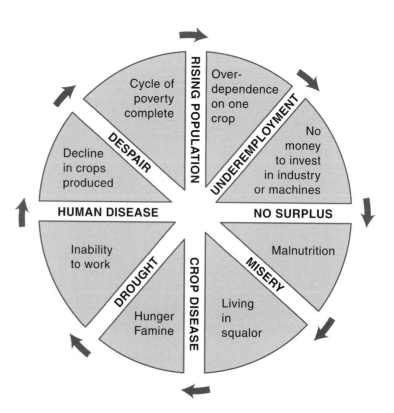

operate at this level of *subsistence farming*, often because they are using pre-industrial technology such as mule-drawn wooden ploughs and planting low-yield, disease susceptible and unfertilised crops, never produce a surplus that they can convert into cash in order to buy more modern farming technology.

Definitions of poverty

Poverty is defined in relation to the *average* wealth of a country. In many poor countries such as India and some South American countries, some people are extremely rich and some areas are heavily industrialised and intensively farmed. But these conditions are not uniformly spread throughout the countries as a whole and there is a great contrast between the rich and the poor.

The average wealth of different countries, however, can be measured against each other statistically. Countries produce wealth through agriculture, mining, industry and trade. This total is referred to as the gross domestic product (GDP). But countries also have other financial activities, such as banking and insurance, which generate national and international revenues. This added to the GDP produces the gross national product (GNP). If you divide the GNP by the population of a country, you can work out the average wealth produced by each individual. In 1998, Bangladesh, for example, had a GNP of less than $150 per head, while the USA had one of over $7000 per head.

The effects of poverty

There are many conditions associated with the absolute poverty that affects the lives of about 300 million people worldwide.

- *Malnutrition and hunger*. Many people live on the edge of starvation and do not have properly balanced diets, lacking protein in particular.
- *Disease*. Poor diet and bad water contribute to the many diseases associated with poverty. Diseases such as malaria, sleeping sickness, river-blindness and bilharzia, etc. affect 200 million people annually. Twenty thousand children die every day from diarrhoea.
- *Mortality rates*. The average age of death in ELDCs is between 40 and 50. (In Britain, it is about 70.) This is caused by a high infant mortality rate and the effects of endemic diseases on many adults.
- *Environment*. Many people live in slums in vast urbanised areas such as the shanty towns of Manila in the Philippines, Mexico City and Calcutta. Most of these areas lack clean drinking water, proper sanitation, power for heating, cooking and lighting and community health care or leisure facilities.
- *Illiteracy*. Across the world, 800 million people worldwide can neither read nor write. Many poor countries cannot afford to build schools or pay teachers, but they cannot increase their wealth without a more skilled work force.

The causes of poverty

Physical causes

- *Heat*. Many ELDCs have extremely hot, humid climates which not only make it impossible to work efficiently in the daytime heat but also encourage diseases such as malaria.

- *Desertification*. Due to climatic changes, extensive deforestation of land and other land mismanagement, huge areas of once-fertile land are becoming desert. (The Sahel region in North Africa is a good example of this). This reduces the food-growing and wealth-producing capacity of a particular country. Although other parts of the world also suffer from the climatic and physical conditions described below, the difference lies in the economic capacity to cope with such conditions. Rich countries cope much better with flood, drought, earthquake, crop failure and the effects of typhoons because they can store or buy in food and technology to reconstruct their society.

- *Lack of natural resources*. Some poor countries not only have the problem of a subsistence level, unmechanised agricultural system, but they have no other natural resources such as oil or other valuable minerals, such as rare metals or coal. (Japan's enormous development with no natural resources is an exception.)

- *The population explosion*. One of the most serious problems facing not just poor countries but the world as a whole, is the problem of increasing population. One million people are added to the population every 5 days and the current total figure is 6 billion. This is not just a cause of poverty but also a result of it. Poor families tend to have the largest number of children, partly because they lack access to family planning information and also because high infant mortality rates encourage the need for several children, so that there is someone to look after the parents when they are old. However, in many developed countries such as Sweden, Switzerland and Japan, there has been a drastic decline in the birth rate, raising concerns about their future capacity to generate enough wealth to maintain current standards of living.

- *Distribution of wealth and resources*. One of the major causes of poverty is the unfair distribution of wealth. Poor countries are often exploited by richer countries who pay very low prices for exports of raw materials and set up unreasonable tariffs to make manufactured goods produced by ELDCs, uncompetitive in price. Powerful multinational companies have engaged in economic *neo-colonialism* by controlling what poorer countries produce and paying very low wages to people desperate for work. International banks have also contributed to the continuing poverty of many ELDCs by lending them vast sums of money, the interest payments on which are quite beyond the capacity of the country to pay. Thus, no spare capital is generated for development. Unfair distribution also applies to crucial resources such as food. Despite the increases in population, there is enough food to go round but it is unfairly distributed. The rich northern hemisphere, for example, has only 25% of the world's population but consumes over 70% of the world's resources.

KEY words

Absolute poverty a condition of life so characterised by malnutrition, illiteracy, disease, high infant mortality and low life expectancy as to be beneath any reasonable definition of human decency

FAO The Food and Agriculture Organisation – a United Nations agency, which is particularly concerned with improving methods of food production through irrigation schemes and the use of high yield, disease-free crops

HDI Human Development Index – a score given to every country by the United Nations Development Programme based on health care, income and average life expectancy.

UNICEF The United Nations International Childrens' Emergency Fund, which is particularly concerned with malnutrition and disease among children and with the development of primary health care through education of mothers

Possible solutions

The Brandt Report suggested that drastic action needed to be taken in order to alleviate the dire conditions in which huge numbers of people lived. Its recommendations included the following:

- an increase to 0.7% of GNP by rich countries to spend on aid to less developed countries (in fact, the contribution of countries such as the USA and the UK has gone down since 1980);
- a diversion of the enormous international expenditure on arms production into improving the quality of peoples' lives instead of trying to destroy them;
- an immediate emergency aid programme to help the worst cases of starvation and disease (short-term aid);
- a massive development programme for agricultural techniques such as irrigation, fertilisation, pest control, crop storage and mechanisation in order to help poor countries to become self-sufficient in food (long-term aid);
- greater support for and emphasis on family planning techniques;
- a drastic re-organisation of the world trading system so that developing countries are not exploited by richer countries in terms of the prices paid for their raw materials and crops, the prices they are charged for manufactured goods or the way in which cheap labour is manipulated;
- a greater emphasis on education programmes in order to improve the possibility of ELDCs competing in the technology race, organising their own international marketing and equipping themselves with the legal expertise to fight corruption in their own countries;
- a reform of the International Monetary Fund, so that poor countries benefit and a cancellation of the huge debts owed to international banks by some countries, which have crippled their chances of development;
- education programmes, which will inform the population of richer countries about the effects of poverty and the need for more international cooperation.

Rich and poor

- Japan contributes a greater percentage (0.32%) of its GDP to foreign aid than any other country.
- During the past 6 years, more people have died of hunger than died in two world wars.
- Developed countries spend twenty times as much on arms as they do on aid.
- Total global military expenditure is £1.5 million per minute.
- The world population doubles every 35 years.
- ELDCs now owe £1.4 trillion in international loans and pay back three times more in interest than is lent in aid annually.

Figure 34.2 Starving children

Activities

① 'Many people talk about the poor. Very few people talk to them.' (Mother Theresa) What measures would you put in place to overcome this criticism?

② 'Charity begins at home.' What arguments could be used to support or oppose the view that we should solve our own problems before we help other countries?

③ Which five courses of action taken by rich countries might be most effective in changing the lives of some absolutely poor people and why?

④ Research the work of one major charitable organisation and describe in detail one major overseas project they have carried out recently.

Specimen exam questions

AS What are the major economic, social and political problems facing economically less developed countries (ELDCs)? How do you think these can be best addressed by both the countries themselves and by external agencies?

A2 What do you understand by the term 'globalisation'? What factors (technological, economic, political) have contributed to this phenomenon? To what extent do you consider globalisation to be to the advantage or disadvantage of most people in the world?

Appendices

Appendix 1: General Studies and Key Skills

Why key skills?

All post-16 students are now expected to reach level 3 in the Key Skills of communication, application of number and information technology. The aim of the Key Skills qualification is to develop and recognise your skills in:

- obtaining and interpreting different types of information
- using, developing and communicating information to meet the purposes of your studies, work or other activities
- effectively presenting the results of your work.

You are required to gain this qualification to help you develop the skills you will need in your working life and/or higher education.

How are they assessed?

Each of the Key Skills units is broken down into three or four main skills associated with that area. For each of these you will need to produce evidence. Evidence you gather during your AS/A2 courses is called a portfolio. You will also be required to take a test, though it is possible that AS General Studies could form your test for Key Skills in communication and application of number.

General Studies and Key Skills

General Studies is an ideal means of developing Key Skills at level 3.

In this Appendix there are three routes to show you how to collect your portfolios in Communication, Application of Numbers and IT through General Studies.

Each route has four tasks with a variety of activities. You only need to follow *one* of the routes. In each route the Key Skills requirements are in bold and the General Studies activities in standard point. At the end of each route is a Key Skills record log, which you will need to go with your portfolio.

Route 1

Task 1 General Studies – science, mathematics and technology

Find out about the Chernobyl nuclear power accident in 1986. Discuss whether the advantages of nuclear power outweigh the disadvantages.

C3.1a **Group discussion on a complex subject**
Have a class discussion on nuclear power (your teacher will have to record your contributions to show that you have reached level 3)

C3.2 **Read and synthesise information from *two* extended documents about a complex subject.**

IT3.1 **Plan, and use, different sources to search for, and select, information required for two different purposes.**
Read Issue 5 (Environmental issues) and Issue 8 (Energy) and write down the arguments for and against nuclear power.
Search the Internet for information on Chernobyl. Make a list of the reasons for the accident and the effects of the accident.
Find a plan of a nuclear power station, either from a book or from the Internet.

C3.1b
and
IT3.3 **Make a presentation about a complex subject, using least one image to illustrate complex points.**
Present information from different sources for two different purposes and audiences. Your work must include at least one example of text, one example of images and one example of numbers.
Combine all your information into a presentation of the advantages and disadvantages of nuclear power, including an OHT of the plan of a nuclear power station.

Task 2 General Studies – culture, morality, arts and humanities

Read Issue 19 ('The nature of culture').

IT3.1 **Plan, and use, different sources to search for, and select, information required for two different purposes.**

N3.1 **Plan and interpret information from two different types of sources including a large data set.**
Formulate a questionnaire for people of a variety of ages and classes to find out the nature of British culture.
Use an encyclopaedia and/or dictionary to find a definition of British culture.
Use Internet chat lines and/or e-mail to receive more answers to your questionnaire.

IT3.2 **Explore, develop and exchange information, and derive new information, to meet two different purposes.**

N3.2 **Carry out multistage calculations to do with amounts and sizes, scales and proportion, handling statistics and re-arranging and using formulae. You should work with a large data set on at least one occasion.**
Analyse the information you have received from the questionnaires, and put your results into a graph or graphs. In the light of your information, decide whether you need to look for more information to be able to answer the question below.

IT3.3 **Present information from different sources for two different purposes and audiences. Your work must include at least one example of text, one example of images and one example of numbers.**

C3.3 **Write two different types of document about complex subjects. One piece of writing should be an extended document and include at least one image.**

N3.3 **Interpret the results of your calculations, present your findings and justify your methods. You must use at least one graph, one chart and one diagram.**
Write an essay on, 'British culture – fact or fantasy ?' Incorporate the graphs into the text and refer to the results and their reliability in reaching your conclusions. It might also be a good idea to use a diagram to show why you think the questionnaire results are reliable or not.

Task 3 General Studies – society, politics and the economy

Read Issue 24, 'Social change' and Issue 32, 'Economic problems'

IT3.2 **Explore, develop and exchange information, and derive new information, to meet two different purposes.**

N3.1 **Plan and interpret information from two different types of sources, including a large data set.**
Use the Internet and/or encyclopaedias to discover the system in the UK and four other EC countries on:
– married couples tax allowances;
– tax allowances for non-working wives;
– child benefit.
Find what information you can from newspapers on tax and the family (*The Times*, *The Guardian* and *The Independent* are available on CD-ROM in libraries).
Interview married couples on their attitudes to tax and the family.
Interview single working people on their attitudes to tax and the family.
Use the information you have discovered on taxation to work out comparative tax burdens. Assume a family with three children and a non-working wife where the husband is earning £40 000 a year. To make the figures comparable, just use the UK tax rates (available on the Internet or the Inland Revenue) for all countries.

C3.3 **Write two different types of document about complex subjects. One piece of writing should be an extended document and include at least one image.**

N3.3 **Interpret results of your calculations, present your findings and justify your method. You must use at least one graph, one chart and one diagram.**

Imagine you are a civil servant in the Treasury. Write a report for the Chancellor of the Exchequer on family taxation policies in the EC, including a chart of comparative tax burdens. Make a recommendation as to which country's policies are best and why they should be adopted by the UK.

A report should be written in formal English under the following headings:

TO:

FROM:

DATE:

CONCERNING:

FINDINGS:

RECOMMENDATIONS:

Task 4 General Studies – science, mathematics and technology

To ensure that you have fully covered N3.2 of the application of number, it is a good idea to answer the maths section of the specimen paper from the board you are entering.

These four tasks cover all the Key Skills requirements and should be entered onto a Key Skills log in the following way:

Key Skills log for level 3

Key skill	Activity	Evidence
C3.1a: Contribute to a group discussion about a complex subject	Class discussion on nuclear power	Teacher's record
C3.1b: Make a presentation about a complex subject using at least one image.	Presentation on nuclear power	OHT and plan of power station
C3.2: Read and synthesise information from two extended documents about a complex subject	Reading Issues 5 and 8	OHTs
C3.3: Write two different types of documents about complex subjects.	Essay on British culture Report on family taxation	Essay, report
N3.1: Plan and interpret information from two different types of source, including a large data set.	Questionnaire on British culture Working out comparative tax rates	Questionnaires, tax rates
N3.2: Carry out multistage calculations to do with amounts and sizes, scales and proportion, handling statistics, re-arranging and using formulae.	Specimen exam paper Maths questions Putting information from questionnaires into graphs	Exam paper Graphs, questionnaires

N3.3: Interpret results, present findings, justify methods. Use at least one graph, one chart and one diagram.	Essay on British culture Report on family taxation	Essay, graphs, diagrams, charts, reports
IT3.1: Plan and use different sources to search for and select information for two different purposes.	Using the Internet and encyclopaedias on culture Reading Issues 5 and 8 and using the Internet on Chernobyl	Questionnaires, OHTs
IT3.2: Explore, develop and exchange information, and derive new information, to meet two different purposes.	Analysing questionnaires on British culture Using the Internet to discuss family taxation	Graphs, tables
IT3.3: Present information from different sources for two different purposes and audiences including text,	Presentation on nuclear power Essay on British culture	OHTs, essay

Route 2

Task 1 General Studies – science and technology

'It is not possible to believe in both science and religion in the twenty first century.' Evaluate the arguments for and against this view.

C3.1a **Group discussion on a complex subject.**
Read Issue 3 ('Scientific method and its application') and then have a class discussion about whether you have to believe in science for scientific method to work (your teacher will make a record of your listening and contributing skills).

C3.2 **Read and synthesise information from *two* extended documents about a complex subject.**

IT3.1 **Plan, and use, different sources to search for, and select, information required for two different purposes.**

N3.1 **Plan and interpret information from two different types of sources including a large data set.**
Re-read Issue 3 and then read Issue 2 ('Religion and science') and make notes on the relationship between science and religion. Prepare an OHT on how religious people manage to believe in both science and religion. Devise a computerised questionnaire for people to say whether they believe only in science, or only in religion, or in both science and religion. Give out at least 50 copies.

C3.1b
and
IT3. 3 **Make a presentation about a complex subject, using at least one image to illustrate complex points.**
Present information from different sources for two different purposes

and audiences. Your work must include at least one example of text, one example of images and one example of numbers.

N3.2 Carry out multistage calculations to do with amounts and sizes, scales and proportion, handling statistics and re-arranging and using formulae. You should work with a large data set on at least one occasion.

N3.3 Interpret the results of your calculations, present your findings and justify your methods. You must use at least one graph, one chart and one diagram.

Prepare the OHT as a word processed text. Tabulate the responses in the questionnaire to indicate the percentage believing in science, the percentage believing in religion and the percentage believing in both. Put the results into an OHT graph/chart/pictograph. Find an image on the Internet (e.g. Darwin) which can introduce a presentation on science and religion. Download it and make it into an OHT.

Make a presentation to the class on your response to the question.

Task 2 General Studies – society, politics and the economy

What explanations can you offer for the prevalence of crime amongst adolescent males? What might be done to reduce the amount of crime committed by this group?

IT3.1 Plan, and use, different sources to search for, and select, information required for two different purposes.

Read Issue 25 ('Crime and deviance') and use the Internet to find explanations of why crime is so prevalent among adolescent males.

N3.1 Plan and interpret information from two different types of sources including a large data set.

N3.2 Carry out multistage calculations to do with amounts and sizes, scales and proportion, handling statistics and re-arranging and using formulae. You should work with a large data set on at least one occasion.

Compile a questionnaire to be given to 20 14–17-year-olds, 20 18–25-year-olds and 20 over-25s on what can be done to reduce adolescent male crime. Analyse your results into a series of graphs.

IT3. 3 Present information from different sources for two different purposes and audiences. Your work must include at least one example of text, one example of images and one example of numbers.

C3.3 Write two different types of document about complex subjects. One piece of writing should be an extended document and include at least one image.

N3.3 Interpret the results of your calculations, present your findings and justify your methods. You must use at least one graph, one chart and one diagram.

Answer the question as an essay, incorporating the graphs into the texts with appropriate comments relating your graphical conclusions to your essay conclusion.

Task 3 General Studies – culture, morality, arts and humanities

Examine the view that all religions serve the same spiritual and social purpose and promote the same basic values. Discuss this view in relation to two different religions with which you are familiar.

IT3.2 **Explore, develop and exchange information, and derive new information, to meet two different purposes.**
Make a separate column for each religion you have chosen. Read Issues 12 ('The nature of religion') and 13 ('Why people have religious belief') to fill in the columns on spiritual purpose, social purpose and spiritual values. Use e-mail, chat lines, etc. to find members of the two religions and ask them their views on the spiritual, social and basic values of their faith. Put your results into a chart.

C3.3 **Write two different types of document about complex subjects. One piece of writing should be an extended document and include at least one image.**
Write a newspaper report, incorporating your chart, to illustrate the view that since religions are so similar, there should be no conflict between them.

Task 4 General Studies – science, mathematics and technology

To ensure that you have covered fully N3.2 of the application of number, it is a good idea to answer the maths section of the specimen paper from the board you are entering.

These four tasks cover all the Key Skills requirements and should be entered onto a Key Skills log in the following way:

Key skills record log for level 3

Key skill	Activity	Evidence
C3.1a: Contribute to a group discussion about a complex subject.	Class discussion on scientific method	Teacher's records
C3.1b: Make a presentation about a complex subject using at least one image.	Presentation on science and religion	OHTs
C3.2: Read and synthesise information from two extended documents about a complex subject.	Reading Issues 2 and 3	OHTs
C3.3: Write two different types of documents about complex subjects.	Essay on crime, newspaper report on religion	Essay, report

N3.1: Plan and interpret information from two different types of source, including a large data set.	Questionnaires on science and religion, questionnaires on crime	Questionnaires
N3.2: Carry out multistage calculations to do with amounts and sizes, scales and proportion, handling statistics, re-arranging and using formulae.	Analysing results to make graphs on crime and science and religion, doing maths questions on exam paper	Graphs, exam papers
N3.3: Interpret results, present findings, justify methods. Use at least one graph, one chart and one diagram.	Presentation on science and religion, essay on crime	OHTs, essay
IT3.1: Plan and use different sources to search for and select information for two different purposes.	Reading Issues 2 and 3 on science and religion, reading Issue 24 and using the Internet on crime	OHTs on science and religion, essay on crime
IT3.2: Explore, develop and exchange information, and derive new information, to meet two different purposes.	Questionnaires on crime, reading Issues 12 and 13 using e-mails and chatlines on religion	Questionnaires and graphs, chart on religion
IT3.3: Present information from different sources for two different purposes and audiences including text, numbers and images.	Presentation on science and religion, essay on crime	OHTs, essay on crime

Route 3

Task 1 General Studies – culture, morality, arts and humanities

'I know what I like and that's all there is to it.'
Why is such a response to a work of art probably inadequate?

C3.1a **Group discussion on a complex subject.**
Have a class discussion on what criteria should be used when judging a work of art. Make notes of the comments made (your teacher will keep a record of your listening and contributing skills).

C3.2 **Read and synthesise information from *two* extended documents about a complex subject.**

N3.1 **Plan and interpret information from two different types of sources including a large data set.**

N3.2 Carry out multistage calculations to do with amounts and sizes, scales and proportion, handling statistics and re-arranging and using formulae. You should work with a large data set on at least one occasion.

Read Issues 18 ('Aesthetic evaluation') and 21 ('Creativity and innovation') and the notes from the class discussion to compile a list of criteria for judging a work of art. Make your criteria into a computerised OHT.

Interview at least 50 people, or compile a questionnaire and give it out to 50 people, to ascertain their agreement/disagreement with the quotation. Convert the answers into a computerised statistical chart.

C3.1b and IT3.3 Make a presentation about a complex subject, using at least one image to illustrate complex points.

Present information from different sources for two different purposes and audiences. Your work must include at least one example of text, one example of images and one example of numbers.

N3.3 Interpret the results of your calculations, present your findings and justify your methods. You must use at least one graph, one chart and one diagram.

Make a class presentation of your view of the question using your OHT and the statistical chart.

Task 2 General Studies – science, mathematics and technology

What are the main sources of air pollution in present-day Britain, and what measures are being, or could be, taken, to improve air quality?

Read Issue 5 ('Environmental issues'), newspapers, CD-ROMs and the Internet to discover the main sources of pollution in Britain. Present your findings in a computerised chart.

N3.1 Plan and interpret information from two different types of sources including a large data set.

N3.2 Carry out multistage calculations to do with amounts and sizes, scales and proportion, handling statistics and re-arranging and using formulae. You should work with a large data set on at least one occasion.

Read Issue 8 ('Energy') and use the Internet to discover measures that are being, or could be taken, to improve air quality. Use the Internet, and possibly e-mail, to discover the relative costs of the different measures and convert your findings into a graph or statistical chart.

IT3. 3 Present information from different sources for two different purposes and audiences. Your work must include at least one example of text, one example of images and one example of numbers.

C3.3 Write two different types of document about complex subjects. One piece of writing should be an extended document and include at least one image.

N3.3 Interpret the results of your calculations, present your findings and justify your methods. You must use at least one graph, one chart and one diagram.

Answer the question as an essay including the graph/chart and a computerised image of one of the measures to improve air quality.

Task 3 General Studies – society, politics and the economy

Some social attitudes and values change from one generation to the next, whereas others appear fairly constant. To what extent do you expect your standards and priorities to differ from those of your parents?

IT3.2 Explore, develop and exchange information, and derive new information, to meet two different purposes.

Read Issues 23 ('The nature of society') and 24 ('Social change') and make a list of social attitudes and values. Put these onto a spreadsheet showing your views and your parents' views.

Using the information on the spreadsheet, write a time capsule letter for your children/grandchildren, explaining how attitudes have changed between you and your parents. This should be written in a form that enables them to use it in assessing the changes in standards and priorities between them and their children.

Task 4 General Studies – science, mathematics and technology

To ensure that you have fully covered N3.2 of the application of number, it is a good idea to answer the maths section of the specimen paper from the board you are entering.

These four tasks cover all the Key Skills requirements and should be entered onto a Key Skills log in the following way:

Key Skills record log for level 3

Key skill	Activity	Evidence
C3.1a: Contribute to a group discussion about a complex subject.	Class discussion on judging a work of art	Teacher's records
C3.1b: Make a presentation about a complex subject using at least one image.	Presentation on work of art	OHTs and teacher records
C3.2: Read and synthesise information from two extended documents about a complex subject.	Reading Issues 18 and 21 and synthesising into an OHT	OHT
C3.3: Write two different types of documents about complex subjects.	Essay on air pollution, time capsule letter on standards	Essay, letter
N3.1: Plan and interpret information from two different types of sources including a large data set.	Questionnaire on art criteria, investigating relative costs off antipollution measures	Questionnaires, graph or statistical chart

N3.2: Carry out multistage calculations to do with amounts and sizes, scales and proportion, handling statistics, re-arranging and using formulae.	Converting questionnaires into a statistical chart, converting relative costs into a graph, exam paper questions	Statistical chart, graph, exam paper
N3.3: Interpret results, present findings, justify methods. Use at least one graph, one chart and one diagram.	Class presentation on works of art, essay on air quality	OHTs and teacher records, essay
IT3.1: Plan and use different sources to search for and select information for two different purposes.	Reading Issues 18 and 21 and class discussion, converting into OHT, questionnaire on art	OHT, questionnaires
IT3.2: Explore, develop and exchange information, and derive new information, to meet two different purposes.	Reading Issue 8 and using Internet, e-mail to find relative costs	Statistical chart
IT3.3: Present information from different sources for two different purposes and audiences including text, numbers and images.	Work of art presentation, essay on air quality	OHTs and teacher

Route 4

Task 1 General Studies – culture, morality, arts and humanities

Outline the various factors that contribute to our notions of right and wrong. To what extent is it possible to tolerate differences of opinion about such matters?

C3.1a **Group discussion on a complex subject.**
Have a class discussion on whether there is a need for people living in society to have agreement about what is right and what is wrong (you will need to make notes and your teacher will record your listening and contributing skills).

C3.2 **Read and synthesise information from *two* extended documents about a complex subject.**

N3.1 **Plan and interpret information from two different types of sources, including a large data set.**
Read Issues 14 ('The need for morality and the nature of ethical theories') and 15 ('Rights and responsibilities') and analyse the factors contributing to ideas of right and wrong. Make your analysis into a computerised OHT.

IT3.1 **Plan, and use, different sources to search for, and select, information required for two different purposes.**

N3.2 Carry out multistage calculations to do with amounts and sizes, scales and proportion, handling statistics and re-arranging and using formulae. You should work with a large data set on at least one occasion
Construct a questionnaire on occasions when it is permissible to break the law. Analyse your results into a frequency table and a graph showing the interquartile range.

C3.1b
and
IT3. 3 Make a presentation about a complex subject, using at least one image to illustrate complex points.
Present information from different sources for two different purposes and audiences. Your work must include at least one example of text, one example of images and one example of numbers.

N3.3 Interpret the results of your calculations, present your findings and justify your methods. You must use at least one graph, one chart and one diagram.
Make a class presentation on the question using your OHT and the frequency table and graph.

Task 2 General Studies – society, politics and the economy

How important and useful do you consider the new Key Skills and General Studies to be in post-16 education? How effective and essential are they in promoting greater breadth of study in the curriculum?

IT3.1 Plan and use different sources to search for and select information required for two different purposes.
Use the QCA and/or the AQA/Edexcel/OCR websites to find the criteria for General Studies and Key Skills. Use this information to work out why they might be useful and/or important for post-16 education.

N3.1 Plan and interpret information from two different types of source, including a large data set.

N3.2 Carry out multistage calculations to do with amounts and sizes, scales and proportion, handling statistics and re-arranging and using formulae. You should work with a large data set on at least one occasion.
Devise questionnaires for A1 students, A2 students and teachers on the effectiveness and usefulness of General Studies and Key Skills in promoting greater breadth of study (i.e. six tally charts). Analyse your results into at least two graphs.

IT3. 3 Present information from different sources for two different purposes and audiences. Your work must include at least one example of text, one example of images and one example of numbers.

C3.3 Write two different types of document about complex subjects. One piece of writing should be an extended document and include at least one image.

N3.3 Interpret the results of your calculations, present your findings and justify your methods. You must use at least one graph, one chart and one diagram.
Answer the question as an essay, incorporating, and referring to, your two graphs.

Task 3 General Studies – science, mathematics and technology

What do you understand by the term 'globalisation'? What factors (technological, economic, political) have contributed to this phenomenon?

C3.3 **Write two different types of document about complex subjects.**

IT3.2 **Explore, develop and exchange information, and derive new information, to meet two different purposes.**

Find different dictionary definitions of globalisation. Use Issue 11 ('The impact of science on culture'), interviews and class discussion to sort out the technological, economic and political factors.

Imagine you are a research consultant for a large multinational firm. You have been asked by the Managing Director/Chief Executive to write a report identifying the most important factor contributing to globalisation. You should write your report in the format suggested in Route 1.

Task 4 General Studies – science, mathematics and technology

To ensure that you have fully covered N3.2 of the application of number, it is a good idea to answer the maths section of the specimen paper from the board you are entering.

These four tasks cover all the Key Skills requirements and should be entered onto a Key Skills log in the following way:

Key Skills record log for level 3

Key skill	Activity	Evidence
C3.1a: Contribute to a group discussion about a complex subject.	Group discussion on right and wrong	Teacher records
C3.1b: Make a presentation about a complex subject using at least one image.	Presentation on right and wrong	OHTs, graphs and teacher records
C3.2: Read and synthesise information from two extended documents about a complex subject.	Read Issues 14 and 15 and synthesise into OHT	OHT
C3.3: Write two different types of documents about complex subjects.	Essay on General Studies, report on globalisation	Essay, report
N3.1: Plan and interpret information from two different types of sources including a large data set.	Prepare questionnaire on breaking the law and analyse, prepare questionnaire on General Studies and analyse	Questionnaires
N3.2: Carry out multistage calculations to do with amounts and sizes, scales and proportion, handling statistics, re-arranging and using formulae.	Analysis of questionnaires on law into graphs, analysis of questionnaires on General Studies into graphs, exam paper	Tally charts and graphs, frequency tables, exam paper

N3.3: Interpret results, present findings, justify methods. Use at least one graph, one chart and one diagram.	Presentation on right and wrong	OHTs and teacher records
IT3.1: Plan and use different sources to search for and select information for two different purposes.	Questionnaire on right and wrong, questionnaire on General Studies	Questionnaires
IT3.2: Explore, develop and exchange information, and derive new information, to meet two different purposes.	Analysing results of questionnaires on GS into graphs, using dictionary, Issue 10 interviews, etc. on globalisation	Graphs, notes on technological, economic and political factors Report
IT3.3: Present information from different sources for two different purposes and audiences including text, numbers and images.	Class presentation on right and wrong	OHTs and teacher records

Appendix 2: Answering General Studies questions

This section of the book is designed to cover each of the different question types you will encounter in the examinations and gives general advice on how to tackle them.

Essay questions (AQA A and B, Edexcel, OCR)

Essay topics in General Studies are usually broader than those set in specialist subjects. They are also likely to have several aspects to them, all of which must be addressed if you are to gain good marks. You may be required, for example, to consider the arguments for *and* against a particular case to demonstrate your full understanding of the issues. Specific knowledge, ideas and opinions are important, but the points you make should not be too technical or one-sided. They should take the wider view. Therefore, remember to write in a manner appropriate to 'the intelligent general reader', as the AQA A instruction says.

Also, you should be aware that one key assessment objective in General Studies, which will often be present in the essay questions, is to test your ability to reflect on the nature of the knowledge related to the question, how we know what we know, and its limitations.

Choosing the topic

In most cases, you will be given a choice of essay titles, so the first thing you have to do is to make your choice.

Good reasons for choosing a topic are:

- an understanding of the question and its purpose
- an interest in and well-formed opinions on the topic. Have you thought about the question and related issues before?
- an ability to address *each part* of the question
- adequate knowledge, ideas, examples and illustrations to provide a worthwhile answer.

You are unlikely to produce a good answer if you have never thought seriously about the question before!

As part of the process of choosing and answering an essay question, it is often a good idea to underline the key elements of the question, e.g. *What <u>literary qualities</u> help to make a book '<u>a good read</u>'? Refer to at least <u>two specific examples</u> of literature you have <u>particularly enjoyed</u>, and <u>explain the nature of the enjoyment</u> you have gained.*

This helps to make sure that you address all parts of the question in your answer.

Planning your answer

When you have decided on your topic, you *must* draw up a plan of your answer. There are several ways of doing this, e.g. brainstorming, a scattergram or spidergram, but all involve a form of listing or setting out your ideas. If you have 40 minutes or so for your answer, then at least 10 minutes should be spent on preparing your ideas before you start to write. This has the advantage of allowing for new details to come to mind as you form your plan, before you finally commit yourself, and as you write your answer. It will also help to show whether you have made a worthwhile choice, or should try another question.

Executing your answer

Try to follow a sequence:

- Decide exactly what your major points, arguments and references are going to be.
- Organise these in a convincing sequence, using paragraphs properly and effectively (each developing *one* distinct area only).
- Introduce your main theme(s) and intention in a brief opening paragraph. Attempt to define any key terms and concepts clearly.
- Introduce appropriate arguments supported by information, references and illustrations relevant to the question (not too many, not too detailed, not too few). In General Studies, try to move from the general to the particular and back.

- Write in reasonably short, punchy sentences, using appropriate connecting language, e.g. 'in addition', 'however', 'therefore', to improve fluency.
- Make sure you have covered what you intended and have come to a clear conclusion.

There are some typical pitfalls in General Studies questions.

- There is a tendency to forget that the question is almost certainly a general one and pitch straight into a reproduction of a specialist answer based on work learned for another A-level subject. You should be careful how you use your material. Do not simply write down everything you know about the subject, regardless of the question. This may seem exceedingly obvious, but it is a common fault. In their enthusiasm or panic, many candidates fall into this trap.
- It is tempting to twist what you know artificially to fit the question, but this will be unconvincing and lead to irrelevance.
- Candidates often spend too much time going into specialist or technical detail, so that little overall analysis emerges relating to the general question. This is very common. Retelling the whole story, or describing all the theory or detail of a topic, is usually not required beyond an outline summary or reference to points required to answer the question. You should resist the temptation just to keep on writing without referring back to the question and your answer plan.
- Consider arguments or points in isolation from each other, so that the answer consists of several parts with little or no links between them. You should try to integrate your ideas and illustrations, moving easily from the general to the particular and back. This depends on having a clear idea of what you want to say in the first place and of where the essay is leading at each stage.

Summary

- Always prepare a proper essay plan before you start to write.
- Always try to identify the extra or different dimension of General Studies.
- Always use material from your specialist subjects carefully to meet the demands of the question.

Checking your answer

When you have finished writing your essay, always try to check it for errors. It is also useful to evaluate it from a general point of view by asking yourself the following checklist of questions.

- Have I addressed all the requirements of the question?
- Have I defined my aims and outlined my plan at the beginning?
- Have I begun my essay in a way that will make the reader want to read on?
- Have I written in clear paragraphs?
- Does each paragraph elaborate on one distinct idea?
- Have I got the right number of ideas for this length of essay – not too few and not too many?
- Have I used appropriate connecting expressions to make my sequence of thoughts clearer to the reader?
- Does my essay do what it says it is going to do?
- Have I come to a clear conclusion?

Comprehension and evaluation of stimulus material (AQA A and B, Edexcel, OCR)

All the General Studies examinations have questions in them that require you to analyse, interpret and comment on a variety of material, some including data as well as text, to demonstrate your understanding of the issues, the nature of the different arguments and points of view presented and their source and validity. You should pay particular attention to the relative merits of different arguments and evidence and such concerns as the degree of objectivity, neutrality or bias that may be present in any of the sources.

Always approach the test in a systematic way, as you will usually be working under pressure of time. You should follow this sequence.

- Scan all the material relating to the test as a whole, including the questions, so that you gain a quick idea of what the content is about.
- Read all the stimulus material carefully, trying to work out what the text is attempting to cover and the general points conveyed. At this stage you should be focusing on the key points and the main thread of the arguments. Underline what appear to be the key points or topic sentence(s) in each part as you go.
- Work through each of the questions in turn. Think through your answer before you write. The question paper will give you the number of marks allotted to each question and this should give you an idea of how much you need to write. If one mark only is being given, maybe even one word will do, unless it is clear that complete sentences are required. If an answer is worth 3 marks, then you probably need to make more than one statement.
- Use your own words as much as possible to demonstrate that you have understood the material. Merely repeating the words or phrases in the extracts is unlikely to convince the examiner . Avoid the temptation to over-elaborate. This is quite common and you run the risk of losing marks by including marginal or irrelevant points.
- Leave space, if possible, so that you can add ideas that may come to you later. If you feel that a question is too difficult or that you are taking too long over it, move on and return to it later, if you have time. You have to be very disciplined with yourself in an examination to make sure that you use the limited time to best effect. Quite often the inspiration needed to break through a problem comes on its own later, after you have mulled it over in your mind.
- Remember that summaries and extended responses require a brief plan before you write them out in full, but also make sure that a plan is not a full attempt. This will only waste time.
- Check your answers carefully at the end. Make sure that the meaning you intended is clear and that your English is correct.
- If you wish to change an answer, do this as neatly as possible. Draw a single line through plans, rough work or any other material you do not wish to be

marked. Do not obliterate these completely, as sometimes such material can be scrutinsed by an examiner to the candidate's benefit.

Multiple choice questions (AQA A and Edexcel)

These may be comprehension questions based on a variety of material, mostly articles with related diagrams and data, or they may be stand-alone scenarios and problems. Such items are designed to test a wide range of knowledge and understanding quickly, so speed and concentration are essential when you tackle these.

Follow this sequence:

- Scan all the material relating to the test as a whole, including the questions, so that you gain a quick idea of what the content is about.
- Read all the stimulus material carefully, trying to work out what the text is covering and the main points conveyed. At this stage you should be focusing on the key points and the main thread of the arguments. Underline what appear to be the key points or topic sentence(s) in each section as you go.
- Work through each of the questions in turn. Think through your answer before you indicate what you consider to be the correct response.
- Speed and decisiveness are essential. Objective or multiple choice tests are designed to cover a lot of ground in a short period of time. Usually the questions are worth equal marks (1 only), whether they are easy or difficult. In the AQA tests you have about 35 minutes in total to complete these (45 minutes at A2), so this means that you should spend the first 7 minutes or so on steps 1 and 2. You then have approximately 1 minutes to spend on each of the 25 questions, with 3 minutes to review your answers at the end.
- Do not expect to get all the questions right, even if you are aiming at or have hopes of a Grade A. Pass quickly over those items which leave you 'floored', and concentrate on the ones that you feel you ought to be able to get right.
- Concentrate hard but briefly on the question in hand. If the question points you to a particular part of a passage, this is where the answer will be. Do not become distracted by the questions you have passed over or have not yet done. Do not panic. Some of the questions are designed to be beyond all but the best candidates. Be decisive, and try not to change your mind. If you are unsure, go with the answer you first thought was right.
- Return to the more difficult items at the end and try to eliminate the less likely alternatives. Use your deductive powers to reduce the element of guesswork.
- Answer all the questions. Marks are not deducted for incorrect answers, so you have nothing to lose, if all else has failed, by resorting to guesswork. Despite this, every year there are some candidates who fail to attempt some of these questions. Ultimately, A-level examinations are competitive and for some candidates (several hundred in General Studies) one mark is the difference between passing and failing!

Case study (AQA A Unit 6)

For this test you will be issued with a collection of material for study *in advance* of the examination. This will be issued up to *2 weeks before* the written test, to allow you sufficient time to become fully acquainted with the material and the broader issues that it raises. You will be required to work on this material on your own, using your own resources. Your teachers will not be allowed to teach directly to it or to issue notes relating to it, but you may seek help from other sources.

Typically, the material will contain:

- a collection of articles based on one or more of the 'big' themes specified for the module
- material from different sources, representing different viewpoints
- some elements that link different subjects, and quite possibly
- some statistics and tables of data.

Up to *3 hours* of study is recommended prior to the written test, which should be sufficient for you to become familiar with the detail and the main thrust of each extract. In your preparation, you should:

- ensure that you understand key vocabulary, terms and concepts
- summarise for yourself, and in your own words, the main themes and arguments
- draw points together from the different extracts
- make connections and comparisons between them
- analyse the data to establish what they reveal in their own right
- consider the extent to which they support or contradict ideas and arguments presented in the extracts
- evaluate the contribution each makes to the larger picture
- determine what major issues and questions are raised by the material.

In the examination, the questions will test your ability to:

- show your broad understanding of the material
- summarise the points and arguments contained within the extracts
- recognise the connections between the different elements of the subject
- identify the different standpoints and values represented, and
- exercise your own judgements and knowledge on the nature of the arguments and problems.

Questions relating to statistical data will test:

- your appreciation of their use in the context of a broader set of issues
- your understanding of what they reveal in terms of support or otherwise for arguments presented, and
- your evaluation of the validity of conclusions that may be drawn.

Answers to the questions will involve continuous writing, mostly of an extended kind, including *one* essay from a choice of titles drawn from themes related to or raised by the case study material. In your preparation, you should give some thought to what these broader questions might be. Use the advice provided earlier in this section about planning and writing examination essays and extended writing based on material for comprehension. You should take into account the weighting and relative proportions of marks allocated to each question and allot your time accordingly. In the specimen examination material for this test, 35 marks are allocated to the case study questions and 25 marks to the essay. Also, remember the assessment objective in General Studies, which is designed to test your ability to reflect on the nature of the knowledge related to the topic, how we know what we know, and what are its limitations.

Problem-solving exercise (AQA B Unit 4)

This is like a comprehension exercise, except that the problem(s) presented in either the examination or coursework scenarios will almost certainly be ones involving a clash of interests, priorities, values, rights and responsibilities, and some form of moral dilemma.

In that sense, there may be no one right answer and it will be down to you to analyse and comment on the nature of the problem, the conflicting rights and responsibilities of those involved, the justification or otherwise for the actions that were or should be taken, and to present your considered suggestions for resolving the problem.

You may be asked one of several things:

- Write a report or account of an incident, where the emphasis will be on the accurate analysis and logical sequence of the detail.
- Comment on the nature and show understanding of the problem and its complexity.
- Explain the different standpoints that may be adopted, how legitimate you consider them to be and what their limitations are, considering such factors as individual rights and responsibilities to others.
- Propose ways of resolving the problem(s). Here you will be assessed on how thoughtful, appropriate and realistic your ideas are to reconcile the conflicting issues in the best way possible.

Short-answer questions

Short-answer questions are designed to test your knowledge of the specification and your communication skills. They have no data for you to read, carry a mark of below ten and seem to require an answer of about two paragraphs' length. When answering such questions, you should:

- work out how long you have to answer each question (3–4 minutes = one paragraph – it is a good idea to work this out on specimen papers)
- analyse the question to make sure you are answering exactly what the

question is asking for (you do not have the time to waffle – your answers must be short and to the point)
- jot down the key words of your answer while analysing the question so that you have a brief plan to keep you on track
- where possible, use technical terms or specialist vocabulary, as this will increase your mark
- try to finish in the expected time and at the expected length.

Example

Explain the meaning of absolute moral value using *two* examples.
This is a question from Edexcel's Unit 1 specimen exam paper. There are three sections in a 1.5 hour paper, so you would expect to spend 30 minutes on each section. Section A has four short-answer questions, so you should write about two paragraphs (there is 7.5 minutes per question).

Answer

An absolute moral value is typical of deontological ethical theories. It is the sort of value that someone is expected to follow, regardless of the circumstances or consequences.

The Ten Commandments are absolute moral values. For example, Christians are expected not to bear false witness, whatever the circumstances. So, because it is an absolute moral value, they could not tell a lie to save someone's life, or even to save the feelings of someone who says, 'Do you like my new hairstyle?'.

The Roman Catholic teaching that abortion can never be allowed is another good example of an absolute moral value. Roman Catholics will not allow abortion, even thought the pregnant person may be a 12-year-old victim of rape or incest. Abortion is absolutely wrong, and no mitigating circumstances can be taken into account; unlike consequentialist ethical theories, such as utilitarianism.

Data response questions

Data response questions are those where you are given a passage, or passages, and are asked questions whose answers are found in, or based on, the passage(s). They are testing your skills of reading, understanding and communication. There are several things to bear in mind when answering such questions.

- Work out beforehand your reading speed. If you are a fast reader, you should read the whole passage(s) first to get a general understanding of it. If you are a slow reader, you should answer the questions as you read the passage.
- Make brief notes (or underline key words) and phrases in the passage) as you search the passage for answers to the question.
- Write up your answer using the notes/underlinings, and, wherever possible, change the words of the passage into your own words.
- If a specific word or phrase from the passage is referred to, read a good way before, and a good way after, the word/phrase, as there may be clues to its meaning.
- Read all the questions to avoid overlapping information in your answers.

Example

Read the following extract from *The Guardian* newspaper for 2 October, 1998.

Paris unites to drive out pollution

It was a good day to be the owner of a vehicle with an odd numbered registration. But as pollution-bound Parisian motorists got to grips yesterday with 'alternate traffic', the question was: which number?

'One, three, five, seven, nine – they are odd numbers, yours is not', said the policeman to a woman in a green Renault Twingo. He could have fined her 900 Francs (£85) but instead ostentatiously handed her a leaflet about the harmful effects of excessive nitrogen dioxide.

'I know what odd numbers are', she snapped, as traffic began backing up behind her on the exit to the ring road at Porte de la Chapelle in northern Paris.

'I don't think you do', said the police officer. 'What is your registration number?'

'162MOX75', she answered. 'Well then,' he said, 'if it was 163MOX75 or 161MOX75 that would be fine. The number that determines whether you are allowed to drive is the last one in the first group of figures.'

It was a rare clash in a day in which 12 million Parisians with sore throats and stinging eyes belied their belligerent reputation and discovered an almost Blairite sense of community spirit.

By last night, after a day of free public transport, alternate traffic and reduced speed limits, the nitrogen dioxide level in greater Paris had fallen well below the 400 microgrammes per cubic metre that sparked the emergency measures on Tuesday night.

The first examples of the day had been Prime Minister Lionel Jospin and his cabinet, turning up for work in electric Peugeots and Citroëns. Yesterday afternoon, the prefect of police for Paris, Philippe Massoni, thanked everyone and said that life could return to normal today.

Gérard Wilfrid, a postman aged 33, noticed an increase in commuters on his train. 'You cannot do this to people from one day to the next. There needs to be a more fundamental change in people's attitudes towards the car,' he said.

But complaining is what Paris life is all about and one off-duty policeman – who would not be named because he was breaking the law on his scooter (registration 1882YR92) – was impressed by the community spirit.

'I am amazed at how good everyone has been – they have not behaved like Parisians at all. Today I have seen people in suits cycling along and talking on their mobile phones. They clearly left the Mercedes at home. That makes me feel a bit sheepish.'

Police reported that only one in six vehicles was in breach of the emergency law, which excludes taxis, delivery vans, cars with disabled parking permits or three or more people inside – and journalists.

All day, radio stations brought news of declining nitrogen dioxide levels and updates on the anticyclone over France which, combined with a depression over Spain, have kept temperatures in the capital at 25°C for 2 weeks, locking in the noxious fumes.

a) What is meant by alternate traffic? [5]
b) Explain the method used to determine whether car owners could drive into Paris. [5]
c) How did Parisian attitudes appear to change for a day? [4]
d) Why did important politicians use electric powered cars? [4]
e) How might some car owners avoid the inconvenience of the restriction? [6]
f) What weather conditions are suggested to exist in an area covered by an anticyclone? [6]

This is a question from the OCR Unit 2 specimen paper. It is one of three questions on the 1.5 hour paper and should therefore take about 30 minutes, although the mark allocation indicates it may be as little as 20 minutes.

Answer

a) Alternate traffic means that only half the cars in Paris are allowed on the roads on any one day, so car drivers are allowed on the roads on alternate days. (It would be easy to write more than this, but then it would be answering the next question.)
b) The method used to determine whether car owners could drive into Paris was based on the registration number of the car, and, in particular, the first three numbers. The last digit in these numbers determines which cars are allowed into Paris, even numbers one day, odd numbers the next.
c) Parisians are usually argumentative and aggressive ('belligerent reputation' in the passage), but on this day, there was little argument and the people seemed to have discovered the type of community spirit associated with Tony Blair's New Labour. They also usually complain a lot, but on this day there was little complaining.
d) Important politicians used electric powered cars because the alternate traffic system had been introduced when the nitrogen dioxide levels had reached over 400 microgrammes per cubic metre. If they had driven in petrol or diesel cars, they would have been seen as adding to the pollution. However, electric powered cars do not produce harmful emissions, so the politicians were seen as obeying the same rules as the rest of the people.
e) Car owners could avoid the inconvenience of the restrictions by carrying at least two passengers with them, by having a disabled parking permit or by being a journalist.
f) It is suggested that in an area covered by an anticyclone, there will be high temperatures all the time, which creates a barrier in the atmosphere so that the poisonous fumes from vehicle exhausts are trapped in one place, causing a type of smog.

Source questions

Source questions are rather different from data response questions. They are testing your thinking and analytical skills. There may be only one passage, or up to four passages, or sources, but the questions will be about types of argument, types of knowledge, working out the stages or form of an argument, justifiability, reliability and validity. It is very important that you should read the introduction and learn the arguments flow chart to decide whether an argument is valid or justified, types of knowledge and types of argument.

Example

Films and morals

James Ferman, the outgoing chief film censor, came clean the other week. Ferman, head of the British Board of Film Classification for 23 years, declared that he wished he had ordered more cuts to be made to the 1994 film *Pulp Fiction* than the one snip – a close-up of an injection – he deemed necessary at
5 the time. He accused the film of glamorising drug abuse and increasing the number of young people who inject heroin.

Ferman suggested that viewers might emulate John Travolta, the star of Quentin Tarantin's film. 'Travolta takes heroin, drives along blissfully happy, picks up Uma Thurman, goes dancing and wins the competition,' summarized
10 the censor – though his synopsis missed the point that Travolta's character is a greasy two-bit hit-man who is shot to pieces with his pants down while sitting on the john. Aspiration is a funny thing.

The arguments over copycat behaviour have been well rehearsed. But Ferman's most interesting comment was that *Pulp Fiction* was 'socially
15 irresponsible' and should therefore have been cut, even though to do so would have been to damage a 'wonderful' film. In other words, the moral values, not just the content, of a film – which breaks no law – should override its qualities as art. But should we ask film-makers to be social workers?

And even if we do demand a measure of responsibility, how are we
20 supposed to judge film-makers? Who is to say which film treats drugs, or violence or sex, in a responsible way, and which invites us to rush out of the cinema and head straight for our local dealer? Do not some movies, *Pulp Fiction* included, demand a more sophisticated response, and acknowledgement that they might tacitly challenge us to repudiate their twisted morality?

25 Many a crusading film proudly wears its heart on its sleeve. For all the sniping at its blatant nationalism, no one could take Steven Spielberg's *Saving Private Ryan* as other than a lesson in the horror of war and the honour of sacrifice (although during the war it would probably have been censored for demoralising the troops). But what of Scorcese's great modern horror story, *Taxi*
30 *Driver*? The film coldly delineates an anonymous urban world of insane violence, without pausing to allow the viewer a brief, cathartic moment of anger, grief or pity. There is no sign of social responsibility in the movie. Scorcese himself has admitted that re-watching it with a younger audience was an uncomfortable experience: their reactions, he said, were not what he
35 expected. Yet to show is to warn.

So what is it about the moving picture that causes such concern? No doubt it still lacks the respectability conferred by age. There is the sheer size of the audience to ratchet up the stakes. There is the greater realism of the cinematic image, the sense of felt life, compounded by the absence of one clear, guiding
40 imagination to whom to ascribe it all – although, says director David Cronenberg, 'Censors tend to do what only psychotics do: they confuse reality with illusion.' Audiences, young ones at least, if you believe a recent survey, are more sophisticated.

45   There is surely something else, though – a stubborn belief that films are mere entertainment for the masses, who must be protected from themselves. Every big movie is now subjected to a battery of test-screenings before audiences painstakingly chosen to represent a cross-section of potential viewers. It is then re-cut, re-cooked and spiced up to please the public palate.

50   Given the enormous cost of big-budget films and the consequent need to please the audience, the average Hollywood extravaganza is unsuited to hand-me-down morality. Other films, those that seek out an audience that demands something subtler, grittier, more real, more inventive, have a hard enough time getting financed, made, distributed and seen, without being judged on their moral probity by unworkable standards.

55   I would not like to suggest that there should be a free-for-all, or that all film-makers can be relied on to be responsible, well-intentioned types. My point is simply this: that high-sounding nostrums like social responsibility are always more complex than they seem. They rest on slippery ground – recent films about the Irish troubles, such as *In the Name of the Father* or *The Devil's Own*, are

60   examples.

     Adrift in our moral gulf, it is natural that some should blame culture for society's ills. It is also inevitable that some should turn on its most popular medium to redress the balance. But we should think twice before hacking the next Tarantino film to bits.

(Adapted from *Films and Morals* by Nigel Cliff in *Prospect*, January 1999.)

This is a passage from an Edexcel Unit 1 specimen exam question.

a) Identify the stages in Nigel Cliffe's argument that film censorship is more complex and difficult than censors imagine.

Answer

The way to answer this is to read through the passage and make notes each time a new point is made. This will give you the main stages of the argument.

* Cliffe first outlines the case made by Ferman as a justification for censoring *Pulp Fiction*.
* He then shows that there is a problem of criteria for film censorship (it would be an idea to give an example of this).
* He then compares *Saving Private Ryan* and *Taxi Driver* to show that both films are antiviolence.
* Finally, he looks at, and dismisses the case for censorship – it would be a good idea to show this by quoting, 'My point is simply this: that high-sounding nostrums like social responsibility are always more complex than they seem.'

b) Identify clearly two types of knowledge or argument that Cliffe uses.

Answer

While answering part (a), you should have noticed that Cliffe uses argument from analogy in *Private Ryan* and *Taxi Driver* and that he uses induction by quoting several flaws in the case for censorship and then making the general conclusion that censorship is wrong.

Cliffe uses knowledge based on moral values, e.g. glamorising drug abuse. He uses subjective knowledge, e.g. when talking about confusing reality with illusion. He uses knowledge based on belief when he quotes the argument that 'the masses must be protected from themselves'.

c) To what extent do you regard Cliffe's conclusion as justified?

This question carries the most marks and so should have the longest answer. The best way of helping you to answer is to refer you to the thinking and analytical skills in the Introduction. You need to apply the flowchart on whether an argument is valid or justified and apply it carefully to Cliffe's argument, using specific quotes from Cliffe to show the reasons, type of knowledge, etc. and come to a balanced conclusion as to whether his conclusion is justified.

Index

A

B

C